## What Are People Saying About the X-tasy Spot?

Debbie Tideman has on-going workshops titled "How to Find the X-tasy Spot" at the Discovery Center in Chicago, Illinois. It is an exciting and unique class and has drawn an enormous response.

*–Robert Wagner*
Director, Discovery Center

Many women have experienced intense sexual stimulation from the cervix (X-tasy Spot). Debbie Tideman is the first to show women and their partners how to access this area reliably.

*–Barbara Kessling, Ph.D.*
best selling author of
*How to Make Love All Night (and Drive a Woman Wild)*
and *Super Sexual Orgasms*

This exciting book has it all! Included are 16 sexy love games and 101 erotic things to do. It has a new way to make love, "The Horizontal Slide Technique." You can even find love coupons called "sextificates" in the back of the book. There is also a separate tear-out section for the man to read on "How to Find the X-tasy Spot."

*-Sue McGarvie, Ph.D.*
Sex Therapist
Talk Show Host, "Sex with Sue"
Ontario, Canada

A thorough and passionate treatment of this subject; this book is certain to excite and stimulate your sex life.

*–Susan Page*
Author of
*How One Of You Can Bring the Two of You Together*

Debbie brings sex wisdom to new heights. She's got the expertise, that's for sure. She's helped thousands of women find the way to help their men please them.

–Jack Johnston
Jack Johnston Seminars
on "The Male Multiple Orgasm"

I have known Debbie for over ten years. She is honest, trustworthy, and dependable. I have had many chances to work with her while she did volunteer work for various ministries. I can verify that she has a heart for helping women improve their marriages.

This topic is one that I feel should be explored, and Debbie has worked hard to show women how to enjoy sex more.

While helping other women reach their full potential, she's busy fulfilling hers. This vivacious 39-year old daredevil enjoys bungee jumping and riding her custom Harley motorcycle.

I endorse Debbie's book as one of the most helpful books on sex. This is new and exciting material presented here. It should be required reading for newlyweds. I also recommend this book for couples who have been married a long time as a way to put the sizzle back into the marriage.

*-Rev. William Fontaine*

Ms. Tideman's book is explicit without being offensive. It teaches about the sexuality of marriage in a frank and wholesome way that is sure to strengthen the marriage bond.

With so many outside influences tearing down this bond, Ms. Tideman's book is a welcomed support. She reminds us of the God-given pleasures of marriage, so often forgotten or made frustrating by lack of knowledge.

Her book fulfills that need for sex education within marriage and goes beyond that to cover new ideas and techniques. Kudos go to her for having the freedom and courage to share them.

*-Jane Cairo, LCSW, ACSW*
Psychotherapist
Author

# The X-tasy Spot

plus:
## A New Way to Make Love
### The Horizontal Slide Technique

## By Debbie Tideman

*The X-Spot Orgasm* was formerly called *The X-tasy Spot plus: A New Way to Make Love, The Horizontal Slide Technique.*

Printed in the U.S.A.

*Inquiries should be addressed to:*
    JETEX Publishing Company
    P.O. Box 388067, Dept. 404
    Chicago, IL 60638

*Questions, comments, suggestions?*
    E-Mail: Xspot1@ibm.net
    Web Page: WWW.safeplace.net/xspot/home.html


10 9 8 7 6 5 4 3 2

ISBN: 0-9642969-0-X

*This is dedicated to the one I love...Jeff*

*He made my dreams and fantasies come true.*

Sex lies at the root of life, and we can never learn to reverence life until we know how to understand sex.

*-Havelock Ellis*

# Foreword

Ecstasy lies deep within each woman. It's called the X-tasy Spot. Learn how to bring yourself to sexual heights only imagined with this newest discovery for women's sexual pleasure.

This simple-to-read, easy-to-do guide will take you through the steps to fulfillment. Eroticism is fun and Debbie Tideman brings a playful exuberance to her new book. At the same time, she speaks frankly to build a comfort level for her readers.

Right from the start, readers will be able to take the steps toward unlocking new heights of ecstasy in themselves. Readers can also turn to her list of 101 erotic ideas for sparking life into their love lives. Drawings and lists highlight the book, helping to guide readers to their untold sexual powers.

# Preface

You may be asking yourself, "Who is Debbie Tideman and what credentials does she have?"

Let me start by telling you about myself. I am a wife, mother, and entrepreneur. I have had the unique opportunity to talk candidly with women about sex while doing in-home lingerie parties for eight years. It broke my heart to hear tales of unfulfilling sex in the lives of 80% of the married women I spoke with.

I wanted to turn that around so my lingerie parties became seminars as I began teaching new techniques on how to achieve hour-long orgasms. As word caught on about the astounding success I had with helping ladies enjoy hour-long orgasms, a talk show host interviewed me on her show. The rest is history.

My wish for this book is to help married women experience fantastic sex. I want you to know that if I can do it, anybody can.

# Acknowledgments

I wish to thank all the special people who helped me take what was in my heart and put it on paper to share with couples all over the world.

First and foremost, my wonderful, strong, and handsome husband Jeff, who made this book possible.

Sharee, my best friend and sister, who helped me when I overextended myself.

My beautiful daughter Tia, who was patient with me when I was busy with this project.

# Disclaimer Notice

Programs of this type, like diet or exercise programs, will not provide the same results for everyone. Do not start any such program without first consulting your medical advisor to be certain that you are in good health and the program will not affect you adversely.

Any application of the X-tasy Spot theory or games is at reader's discretion and sole risk. This book does not constitute medical advice as Debbie Tideman is not a medical doctor. We cannot guarantee the safety or effectiveness of any technique.

If you have had a hysterectomy, you should note that the primary focus of the techniques, the X-tasy Spot Rub and Horizontal Slide Technique, very likely will not provide the desired result for you. However, the remaining chapters and ideas are worth reviewing and experiencing for their own merit.

The sketches of the human body are not anatomically correct. They are for illustration only.

For the sake of simplicity, the writer will assume the reader is a married woman and refer to her partner accordingly.

# ♥ CONTENTS ♥

# How to Use This Book
## to Maximize Your Sexual Pleasure

Right now, make a commitment to read this book within a week. Make a reading schedule and stick to it. Try to find some quiet time when you won't be interrupted.

- Stop and write out the answers to the questions.
- Take plenty of notes.
- Incorporate what you are learning into the bedroom.
- Review this book often.

# Just What Can You Expect from This Manual?

*This book will:*

- Show you how to request what you want sexually from your husband
- Help you let go of your inhibitions
- Show you how to teach your man how to give you hour-long orgasms
- Give you hundreds of erotic ideas to choose from.

*This book will not:*

- Make all your problems disappear
- Make you become a beautiful sex queen
- Solve all your marital problems
- Make you live happily ever after.

An asterisk (*) above a word means if you cannot find this product in your home town, you can order it confidentially using the order form found in the back of this book.

# Daily Study Schedule

## MONDAY
Date: _____
Time: _____

## TUESDAY
Date: _____
Time: _____

## WEDNESDAY
Date: _____
Time: _____

## THURSDAY
Date: _____
Time: _____

## FRIDAY
Date: _____
Time: _____

## SATURDAY
Date: _____
Time: _____

## SUNDAY
Date: _____
Time: _____

**Here is the secret:**

**Forget everything you ever learned about sex!**

# Begin with the End in Mind:

*It takes 21 days to change a habit.*

You can change average sex to super-excellent, hour-long orgasmic sex.

Habit = *Knowledge + Skill + Motivation*

- This book will give you the *knowledge* you need for super fantastic sex.
- You will develop the *skill* necessary to put the concepts into action.
- You have the *motivation*, the desire to increase your sexual satisfaction.

# Chapter 1

## Case Histories

The majority of women I talk to confide that they are not enjoying sex as much as they'd like to. Orgasm seems to be unattainable. After I let them in on a few simple techniques, things change. Here are some of the results.

### *Laurie and Joe*

I attended a dinner party at my friend Tina's plush high-rise apartment. Seated to my right was Tina's cousin, Laurie, and her husband, Joe. They made a handsome couple, newly married and very much in love.

While we were talking, the conversation turned to my discovery of the X-tasy Spot Rub technique. I explained the technique in great detail and they listened intently. When I had finished, they said their sex was "great, couldn't be better" and concluded they must have discovered the secret on their own. I was surprised, for after talking with a thousand people, only one other person had experienced anything comparable to it.

The next day I received a call from Laurie, who had called Tina for my phone number.

"I have something very exciting to tell you," Laurie said. This woman was so happy she could hardly contain herself. "I want to thank you for sharing the X-tasy Spot information with us. We decided to give your technique a try to see if it was really something new.

"The result was fantastic — a prolonged orgasm like none I had ever experienced before!" she exclaimed.

The X-tasy Spot Rub added another dimension to their already satisfying sex life.

## Kay

I have a young, pretty friend, Kay, who is single. She's had many boyfriends and has lived with quite a few of her lovers. We talked about the quality of her sex life.

Considering her vast knowledge of lovemaking and her numerous partners, I thought she might have experienced a cervical orgasm.

"You know," she admitted, "I feel like something is missing, but I can't pinpoint it. I have rather intense sex and I enjoy it, but I don't have strong orgasms."

I asked her directly about orgasms. She answered, "No matter how many men I sleep with or how many times I make love in one night, I never have an all-out orgasm."

So I fully explained the X-tasy Spot Rub technique to her and asked her to let me know what happened. The next time I saw Kay, she was beaming.

"Debbie," she declared, "it worked. For the first time in my life, I felt fully satisfied."

## Diane and Jim

Diane and Jim have been married eight years. They have two children. She's in her thirties, attractive, and maybe ten pounds or so overweight.

One day Diane confided to me that she lacked confidence as a woman. When I questioned Diane about these feelings, she explained, "I feel sexually inadequate because I rarely have a climax. I feel guilty about not giving Jim the satisfaction of pleasing me.

"I've started to make excuses to avoid sex and now I'm worried Jim will resent me."

I reassured Diane. "It's not necessary to have a climax every time," I told her. "Relax and enjoy each sexual experience."

Together we worked out a plan to strengthen their sexual relationship. We decided her first step was to enroll in an aerobics class to tone her body and make it more appealing. She also needed the extra energy and stamina the workout would provide.

I taught her a one-minute sex exercise (see Chapter 10) and suggested she practice it three times a day for the first month. It was January — a time of New Year's resolutions, a good time to make positive changes.

We discussed her diet and eating habits. We talked about eating healthy foods and getting enough iron, calcium, and protein. I recommended she take a vitamin supplement daily and stop eating junk food.

Our second step was that Diane should shop for a few enticing outfits for the bedroom. She bought a very sexy negligee* and ordered the game, "For Lovers Only*."

January 31 was their wedding anniversary and Diane chose that night for a special occasion. She arranged to have their children spend the night at the baby-sitter's home so she and her husband could spend the evening alone.

During dinner she made coy, suggestive remarks to Jim. She set the mood with scented candles, satin sheets, and a fur bedcover. She slipped into her new lingerie, looking slim from a five pound weight loss from the aerobics and the sex exercise. When she surprised Jim with the "For Lovers Only" game, it opened up a new realm of communication about sex as each showed the other just what turned them on. The couple ended the game by making passionate love.

Jim was surprised at how much tighter Diane felt around him. (The sex exercise had worked.) The game had been so sexually exciting that he came right away, so he asked what he could do to please her. Diane brought up the X-tasy Spot Rub technique, and he went to work finding the pleasure trigger.

"All I know is we started out on one side of the room and ended up on the other," says Diane. "How we got there I don't know. It could have been ten minutes or an hour. While I was in that state of continuous orgasm, it was as if time stood still."

Jim later estimated it was about twenty-five minutes of overwhelming orgasm. He was overjoyed to give her such an exploding climax. Diane cried in his arms afterward, relieved once and for all of the fear of being frigid.

## Chapter 2

♥

### Sensuality Quiz

This is a fun quiz which can help you see how adventurous your sex life has been so far. It's an easy test. Just answer the ten questions with a simple yes or no. When you're finished, see the scoring method below and add up your score.

Your score gives you an idea of how to rate your sexual experience. Remember, this book offers many new things to make your sensual rating go up.

### *Sensuality Quiz*

1. Have you ever given your lover a back massage with oil?
   ☐ yes  ☐ no
2. Have you ever used whipped cream for anything other than what it was intended for?
   ☐ yes  ☐ no
3. Did you ever tell your husband your secret sexual fantasy?
   ☐ yes  ☐ no

4. Have you ever made love anywhere really exotic (in an elevator, public park, airplane, at the office, or any other unusual place)?

☐ yes  ☐ no

5. Have you ever taken a long, luxurious bath with your man?

☐ yes  ☐ no

6. Have you ever danced exclusively for your hubby?

☐ yes  ☐ no

7. Do you usually wear sexy lingerie to bed?

☐ yes  ☐ no

8. Does the shopping list for the bedroom include batteries?

☐ yes  ☐ no

9. Have you ever had your G spot rubbed?

☐ yes  ☐ no

10. Have you ever made love hanging from the ceiling in a Taiwan basket?

☐ yes  ☐ no

## SCORE:

Score 10 points for every "yes" answer; 0 points for every "no" answer.

> *90-100 points* —You know how to drive your man wild in bed!
>
> *60-80 points* —You are a woman who enjoys her own sexuality and likes to experience new things.
>
> *30-50 points* —You are an open, warmhearted, sensual woman who is seeking ways to improve your love life.
>
> *O-20 points* — Don't worry, this book can help!

# SEX INVENTORY

Take an inventory of your sex life. On a scale of one to 10, with one being terrible sex and 10 being fantastic, what has your level of enjoyment been for the last year? Circle one.

1  2  3  4  5  6  7  8  9  10

What would you like it to be and why?

_____

_____

_____

_____

_____

_____

_____

_____

_____

_____

Sex has become one of the most discussed subjects of modern times. The Victorians pretended it did not exist; the moderns pretend that nothing else exists.

*-Bishop Fulton J. Sheen*

# Chapter 3

♥

## You Can Have Long-Lasting Orgasms

From day one, people have been making love. There are volumes written on how to do it with pictures from ancient drawings to modern explicit how-to photos, but you've never before seen what you'll see here.

- The X-tasy Spot Rub is not a position—it's a technique. It can be practiced in many positions.
- The X-tasy Spot is not only a spot, but what to do with the spot.
- The X-tasy Spot Rub is not an abstract state of mind or a fantasy.
- The X-tasy Spot Rub is a practical technique that creates a fulfilling, intense, continuous female orgasm terminated only by total sexual exhaustion.

Many medical experts say that women can't have deep vaginal orgasms — that all stimulation felt originates in the clitoris. Yet, every once in a while, a woman has a deep, satisfying, vaginal orgasm that supposedly doesn't exist. This book teaches you how to have this kind of orgasm consistently.

The object of the X-tasy Spot technique is to stimulate a woman sexually by rubbing the cervix. How should the woman be stimulated? The methods are unlimited.

Knowing how to perform this stimulation enables your husband to use gadgets, fingers, penis, and an endless number of positions, whatever works safely for you.

Explore this new discovery — the most fantastic new discovery for women in sexual pleasure since the G spot was detected, more than ten years ago. Like superconductivity in electricity, there is no resistance to overcome — extended orgasms will last as long as you like.

A new frontier of love will open up for you and your lover from the pages of this manual. Work with him, and this book, to get the out-of-this world delirium that is every woman's birthright.

It takes two to tango—and to make love. The more you excite your man, the more he excites you. You will feel very soft, feminine, and satisfied. He will feel powerful and virile for giving you such long-lasting climaxes.

Mealtime would be deadly dull if you had to think up all your own dishes. Get cooking in your sex life, too, with recipes for making love. It isn't hard to satisfy drives—for food or sex. Being a gourmet in either takes work, but it makes life worth living.

Success, it is said, comes from being in the right place at the right time. Learn where the right place is—inside you. It's the X (as in ecstasy) Spot. This book can be your road map to divine sex. So read on and learn the secrets of an exciting sexual relationship focusing on powerful orgasms.

# The X-tasy Spot

There's a new way for women to experience an orgasm. It's called the X-tasy Spot Rub. The X-tasy Spot is like the G spot. It provides an alternative to the clitoris as a means of producing an orgasm. If the G spot can produce orgasms, the X-tasy Spot can do so as well, because they're both connected to the pelvic nerve.

This nerve, associated with the uterine orgasm, is known to produce a different kind of orgasm from that produced by the clitoris. The two kinds of orgasm can be blended. Rubbing and gently moving the X-tasy Spot on the cervix in just the right way brings on extended orgasm. The X-tasy Spot and the cervix are one and the same.

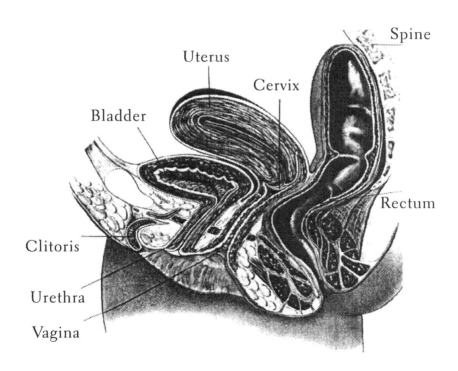

The cervix is the opening to the uterus, or womb. It is located near the top of the vagina. The cervix is connected to and protrudes into the upper end of the vagina. The cervix is the passageway through which a fetus passes into the vagina to be born. According to *The Kinsey Institute New Report on Sex,* the vagina is a small tube about three to four inches long.

The X-tasy Spot is a part of the uterus. It is like the G spot (Grafenberg spot) which is felt through the anterior vaginal wall, because they both produce an orgasm. However, the X-tasy Spot is deeper in the vagina at the cervix.

## The X-tasy Spot Rub

Very few men know the secret to giving a woman an hour-long orgasm. After reading this chapter, you'll possess the secret that will help your husband give you the most intense and deeply satisfying cervical climax you have ever experienced. You can share this secret with your husband by discussing it, by showing him what to do, or by giving him the "Pilot's Checklist" in the tear-out section at the end of this book.

This super inner orgasm is worth the effort needed to find the trigger. It is a continuous climax beyond the multiple orgasm experience. Your husband can keep you in a state of ecstasy for hours.

The X-tasy Spot Rub produces the kind of orgasm that results in a feeling of closeness between yourself and your spouse. This feeling of closeness was given to you by your Creator. This feeling of closeness makes sex meaningful. This feeling of closeness is what you need to cultivate.

There are some necessary preparations. Both you and your spouse must shower or bathe. You should urinate before sex begins since a full bladder causes uncomfortable pressure. Your spouse must be sure his nails are clean and filed short and smooth so that he doesn't scratch you or cause infection.

Lie on your back with your husband kneeling next to you. This is the easiest position for learning the art of continuous orgasm.

Your vagina should be well lubricated. You can use KY-Jelly or a water-soluble flavored gel* for lubrication.

Of course, one of the best methods to provide lubrication is to have intercourse, with both partners reaching a climax. (Don't worry about not being able to climax again. It's been proven that women have the potential to have many climaxes a day.) His sperm deep inside your sexually aroused vagina should help reduce friction.

Your husband should begin by spreading your legs and inserting two or three fingers palm upward into your vagina. At the end of the tunnel, he will find a hard, rounded lump, with a depression or indentation in the middle of the protrusion. This is the cervix, on which the X-tasy Spot is located.

As he deeply probes the vagina, he can fondle the cervix with his fingers. This is called the X-tasy Spot Rub technique.

The key to cervical gratification is pressing firmly like a massage. He can rub his fingers on this X-tasy Spot or around the side of it to gently move the lump back and forth. Lightly rubbing or tapping the indentation of the cervix, increasing pressure in small increments, is one way to find the pleasure point. He must be careful not to push on the cervix too hard.

As you begin your orgasm, there's no need for your spouse to increase speed or pressure on the cervix. The same pressure used to initiate the orgasm will be enough to keep it going. Pushing harder or faster could cause pain, spoiling the effect.

Your husband's fingers can rub and gently move the X-tasy Spot as his thumb stimulates the clitoris. His other hand is free to caress your nipples and other sensitive spots.

Be sure to give your husband direction. Relax, as you discover your erogenous zones together. Express all the sensations you feel. Talk to your honey; tell him when it feels good and if his particular action can make you climax. Talk, breathe heavy, and make noises. Doing so will lessen tension that could cause discomfort.

You will experience overwhelming sensory pleasure from this technique. It's much better than a clitoral orgasm. A clitoral climax reaches a point where further stimulation feels too intense and oversensitive to the touch. No such point is reached during the X-tasy Spot Rub. It goes on and on indefinitely until you are overcome by sheer exhaustion (see diagram on next page).

With the information you now possess, you can prove that the X-tasy Spot technique will give you a better orgasm than you have ever experienced. You will find that the X-tasy Spot is real and it is enormously effective in producing a superior orgasm.

If you experience pain or bleeding, be sure to consult your gynecologist. If you have an I.U.D. or any problems with your uterus, check with your gynecologist before trying this technique.

# Clitoral versus X-tasy Spot Orgasm

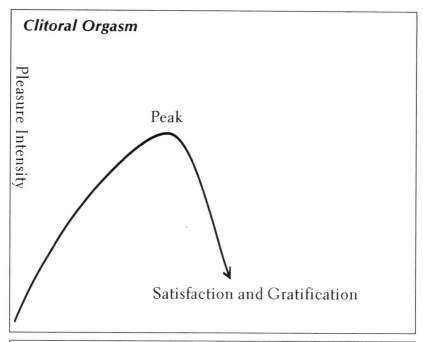

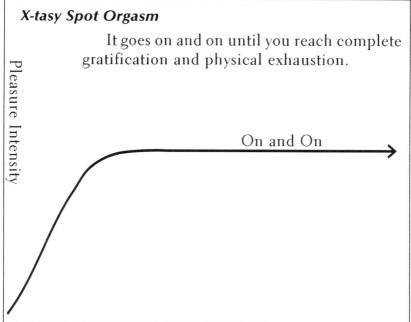

# Variations of the X-tasy Spot Rub

Here are descriptions and drawings of many ways to perform the X-tasy Spot Rub. You're sure to find a few that work best for you.

The following sketches show a cutaway view of the female anatomy to show the different ways the X-tasy Spot can be stimulated. Manually rubbing and gently moving the cervix by hand is the most direct way to have hour-long orgasms.

On the next few pages, four techniques are illustrated:

- •Love Slide
- •X-Massage
- •Love Tug
- •Love Triangle

To show the X-tasy Spot Rub, the X-tasy Spot is called by its proper name, the cervix, as the X-tasy Spot and cervix are one and the same.

# Love Slide

Slide three fingers into the vagina to teasingly bump and caress the tip of the cervix.

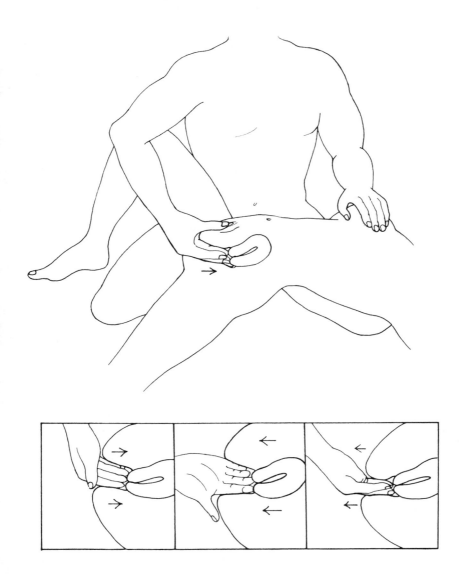

# X-Massage

Find the indentation at the end of the cervix and gently probe it with the middle finger. Then run your finger around the rim. Move the cervix gently back and forth with the finger pressed into the indentation.

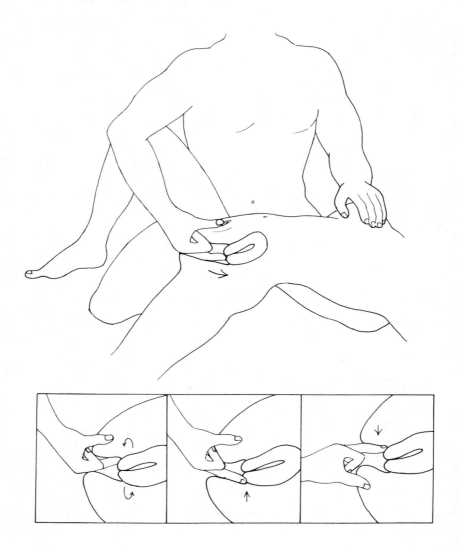

# Love Tug

Lovingly tug on the side of the cervix, moving it back and forth and side to side. Always strive for gently movement of the uterus.

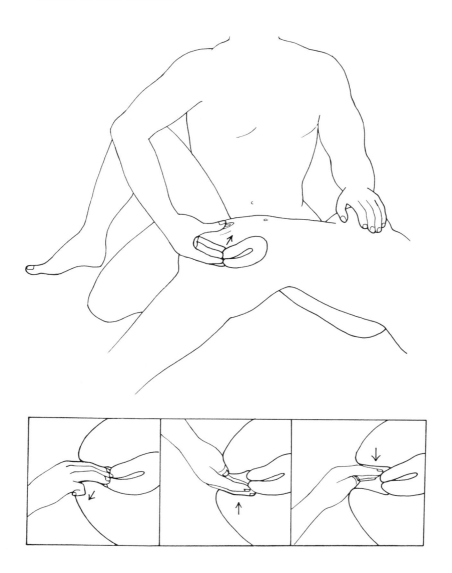

# Love Triangle

Encompass the cervix with three fingers. Move your hand in circles and rotate for the desired effect.

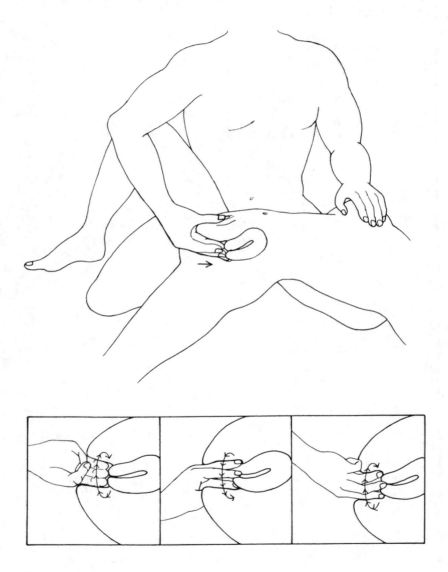

The woman can be face up or face down. If she is face up, your thumb can stimulate the clitoris. Squeezing the pubic bone with a finger stimulates the G spot, while the other three fingers work on the X-tasy Spot.

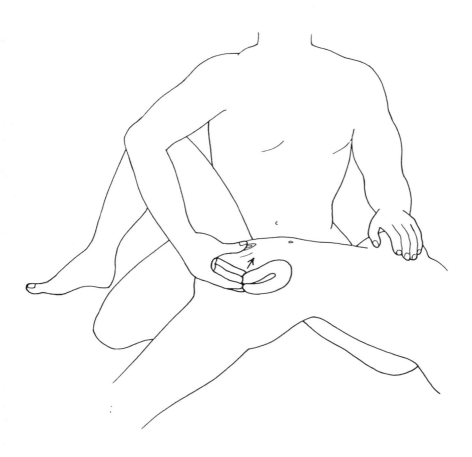

# Face Down, Manual Stimulation

Face down, the pinkie manipulates the clitoris. The ring finger pummels the G spot, the middle and index fingers work the X-tasy Spot, and the thumb can probe the anus, if desired.

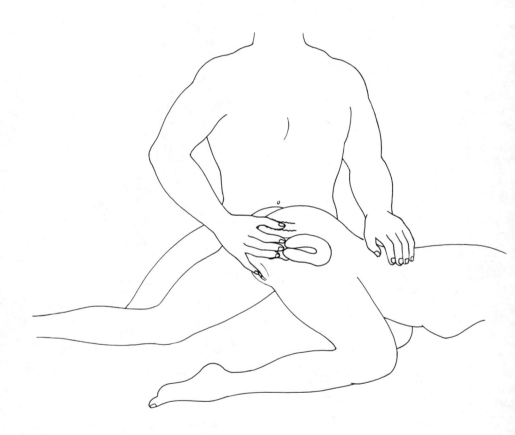

# Chapter 4

♥

## Horizontal Slide Technique

Many sexual positions will stimulate the X-tasy Spot if done properly. Ordinarily, the man thrusts his penis in and out during sexual intercourse. To affect the X-tasy Spot, he must make love differently.

In the Horizontal Slide Technique, the penis is thrust deep inside the woman's vagina; then a horizontal sliding motion by the man, forward-backward, causes the penis to bend up and down, bumping the cervix back and forth.

Start by lying on your stomach, face down. (You may want to start this position kneeling instead.) Your husband enters your vagina from behind, either kneeling or lying on top of you. Once he has deep penetration, he then pushes up toward your head and slides back toward your feet. He keeps his body straight, not pumping with his hips in the ordinary way. At the same time, angle your buttocks up to him as far as you can. A pillow placed under your hips can help. This is a pleasant position because your spouse can caress your breasts or clitoris from behind.

For more power, your lover can push on your underarms to slide toward your feet, and by having you bend your knees, he can push off the back of your knees with his heels to slide toward your head.

Your spouse needs only to slide up and down horizontally while you adjust the angle. A pillow will help you hold the angle once you have found it. In this way, your husband is in the power and speed position, while you fine-tune yourself to put all his effort in just the right X-tasy Spot.

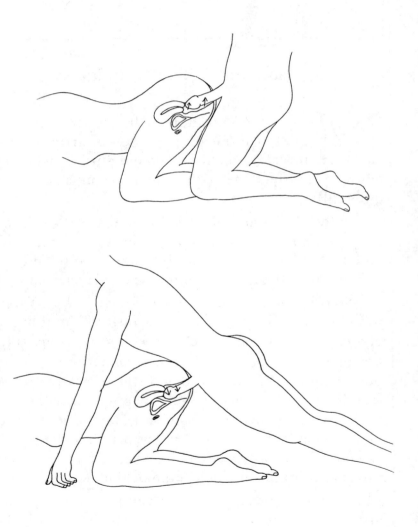

# X-tasy Spot Horizontal Slide

Penis bends down, rubs across end of cervix to the "maximum up" position.

*Heels locked behind knees*

In the "maximum down" position, penis is on top of cervix.

To slide in horizontally, man pushes with legs by locking heels behind her knees; to slide out, push with arms at her shoulder.

Sliding motion causes penis to bend up and down. As the penis pivots on man, it bumps the cervix back and forth, causing a full feeling.

# X-tasy Spot Lever Action

Another angle: Instead of pushing against your under-arm with his hands to slide toward your feet, your husband can reach behind and grab your feet (within easy reach since your knees are bent) and pull to lever your whole body down. Your body moves toward him horizontally. Then he can release you to return to a neutral position and repeat. The lever action multiplies the force.

He slides penis all the way in.
He grabs her ankles.

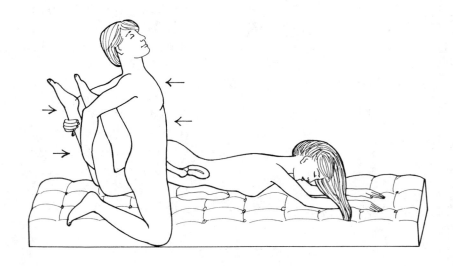

He pulls her ankles. His heels are locked behind her knees. He pushes back with his feet.

Action: Release Pressure
Reaction: Neutral Position Restored

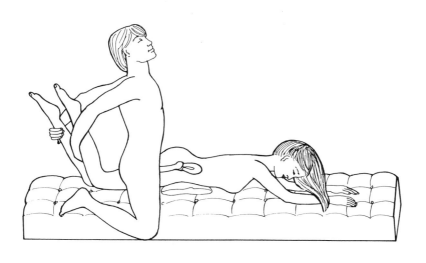

Action: Pull
Reaction: Slide

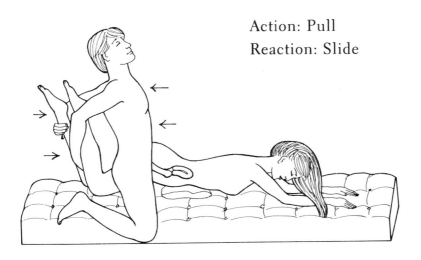

# Positions

*Male from Behind*

There are a variety of positions you can use during one session of lovemaking that hit the X-tasy Spot. Although ladies I must admit, we do not have to move too much to experience an explosive orgasm from an X-tasy Spot Rub. What can be easier?

Start out with woman kneeling with hands on bed. Man kneels behind and enters vagina from behind.

This is a great penetration angle. He can hold her hips and bring her in deeper. The man has lots of control and leverage in this position.

The man has access to her breasts and clitoris in this position.

# Best X-tasy Spot Rub Position

Notice the pillow under her hips to access the right angle.

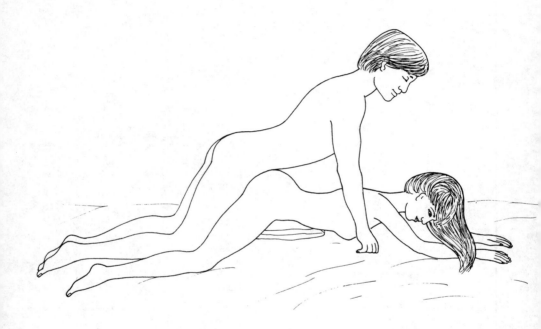

# More Positions that Hit the X-tasy Spot

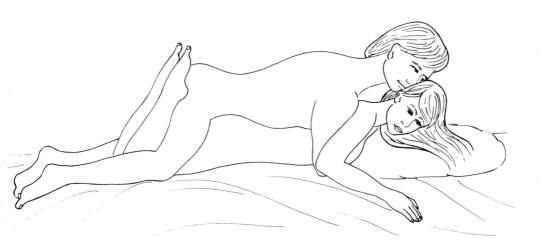

Her legs are on the outside of his hips. Notice the pointed toes; some people tense their bodies as orgasm approaches.

# Ecstasy — X-tasy Spot Orgasm

Elbows on bed, pillow under hips. Knees are bent, legs up, and head is facing forward and up.

## Variations

The bed provides a firm surface to lie on and the drop off at the end of the bed allows easy access for full thrusts to the X-tasy Spot.

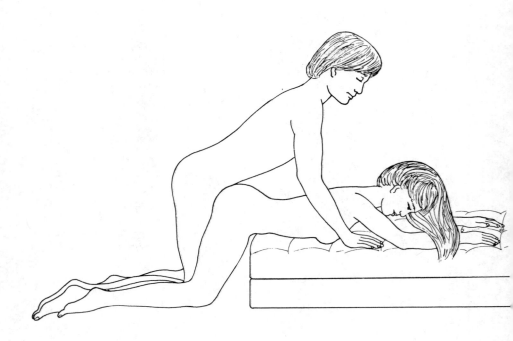

The woman leans on the bed for support as she gets bumped on the X-tasy Spot from behind.

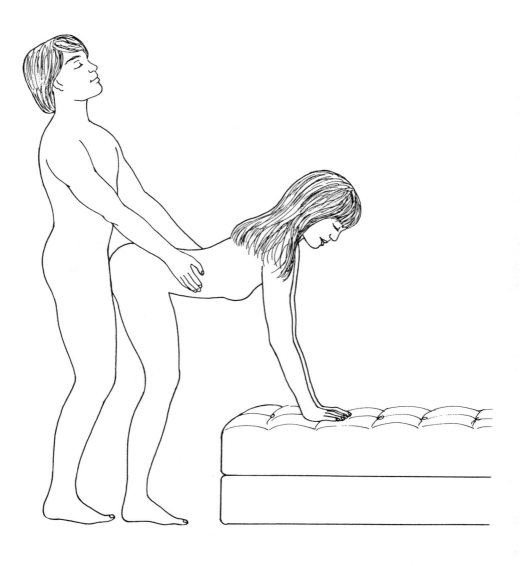

The man kneeling behind the woman who is on a chair,
hassock, or foot stool offers a great angle for deep penetration.

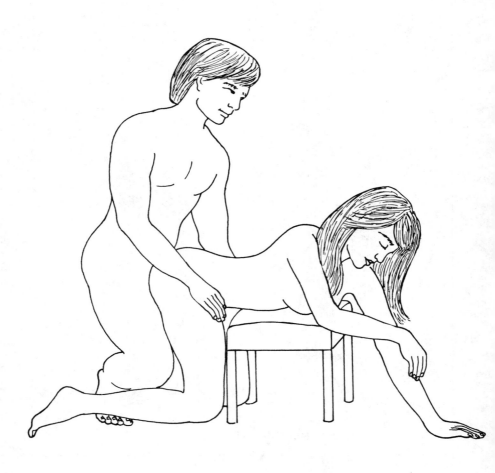

A hammock is excellent since you have leverage to move back and forth and up and down because your feet are on the floor.

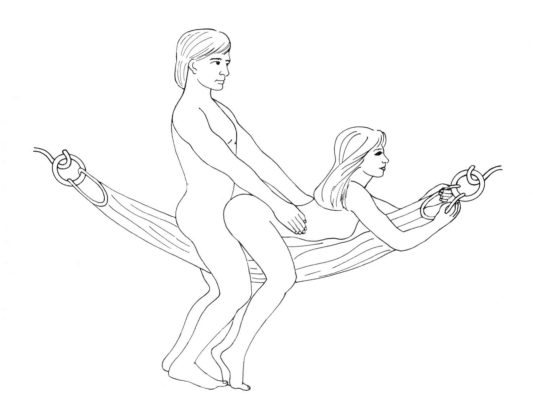

## Chapter 5

♥

### Beyond the G spot

The X-tasy Spot is the successor to the G spot as a means of producing sexual pleasure. It can produce as much sexual pleasure as the G spot, if not more, and it does so differently. It is known that the X-tasy Spot is involved in an orgasm, but it is not so well known that it has been publicly acclaimed.

Freud believed there are two kinds of orgasm, one resulting from clitoral stimulation and the other from vaginal penetration.

The existence and value of the X-tasy Spot has been backed up by research. The X-tasy Spot is recognized in sexual research literature, but this recognition is never made very clear because the purpose of the research was concentrated on other subjects. The existence of the X-tasy Spot can be gleaned from incidental findings from research on other ways of producing sexual pleasure in women. This research is often cited to prove the existence of the G spot. The same research can now be cited to substantiate the existence of the X-tasy Spot.

Research on the G spot can be used to prove the X-tasy Spot's existence; however, the X-tasy Spot cannot be described as concretely as the G spot is described. The G spot is the female counterpart of the male prostate. It lies in the anterior wall of the vagina about two inches from the entrance, directly behind the pubic bone. When the G spot is properly stimulated, it swells and at the moment of orgasm, many women ejaculate a liquid through the urethra that is chemically similar to a man's ejaculation but contains no sperm.

The X-tasy Spot, on the other hand, has no comparable location in a man. It is at the upper tip of the vagina, in the tissue surrounding the opening to the cervix. This is all that the published literature says about the X-tasy Spot. However, what is stated indirectly about the X-tasy Spot gives new meaning to this part of the anatomy.

The X-tasy Spot is also referred to in many contexts. It is known, for instance, that in intercourse, the penis thrusts against the cervix, producing pleasure in the woman. This simple fact is discredited, by Albert Ellis, Ph.D., who talks about the "myth of the vaginal orgasm." Some researchers assert that the cervix does not produce an orgasm. It is acknowledged by others that the cervix can produce pleasure.

Since the cervix is said to have no pain nerves (doctors have told me they can perform surgery on the uterus without using anesthesia) direct pressure might not be felt. However, by moving the cervix, the nerves surrounding it are stimulated, creating a wider zone of pleasure. This explains the feelings of fullness experienced during the X-tasy Spot Rub.

For example, if someone taps her nail on a table top, she can feel it even though the nail itself has no nerves. Because of the nerves connected to the nail, she can feel the movement throughout her fingertip.

The X-tasy Spot is known to have a special property. This is that the X-tasy Spot is connected to the pelvic nerve and the pudendal nerve which innervate the P.C. muscle group.

# Theory of X-tasy Spot

Complete pleasure is sensed all around the cervix, giving a feeling of fullness.

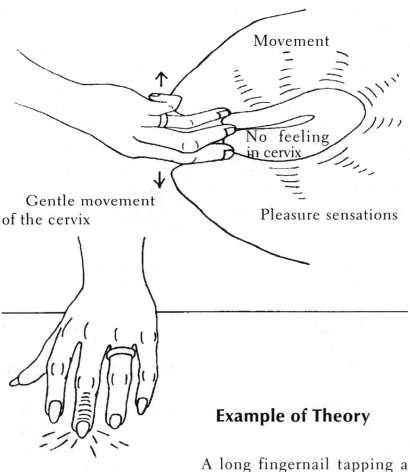

Movement

No feeling in cervix

Gentle movement of the cervix

Pleasure sensations

## Example of Theory

A long fingernail tapping a table top will produce sensations in the fingertip even though the nail itself has no nerves.

The pudendal nerve transmits signals to the P.C. muscles from the brain causing rhythmic contractions of orgasm.

The pelvic nerve is also important because it is believed to be connected to the G spot, as well as other parts of the vagina, uterus, bladder, and lower spinal cord. Since the X-tasy Spot and the G spot are connected by the same nerve and one spot produces a great deal of pleasure, the other can do the same.

The X-tasy Spot's connection to the pelvic nerve is very important for two reasons. First, this nerve is believed to produce a different kind of orgasm than does the pudendal nerve. Second, the two nerves can, operating together, produce a third kind of orgasm, a blended orgasm. These three kinds of orgasm have been recognized for nearly two decades.

This contrasts with the conventional view of female orgasm, held by Masters and Johnson. These authors maintained, since their landmark book in 1966, that there is just one kind of orgasm: the clitoral, or vulval, orgasm. Their research assumed from the start that there was only one kind of orgasm. As a result, they never attempted to measure more than one source.

Bioenergetic analysts use the word "climax" to describe muscular contractions localized in the genitals (usually produced from clitoral stimulation) and the word "orgasm" to describe contractions that spread throughout the whole body (usually produced from vaginal stimulation).

More recent research has shown that there is more than just the clitoral climax. In 1980 Perry and Whipple identified more than one place in the vagina where female orgasm can occur. The new research demonstrates that the three kinds of orgasm can be placed along a single continuum. Table 1 indicates that the three kinds of orgasm are similar in some ways and different in others. The third kind of orgasm, or blended orgasm, is a mixture in varying degrees of the other two kinds. This table also indicates that the cervix is one of several spots that are responsive to sexual stimulation.

## The Perry and Whipple Continuum of Orgasmic Response

The column on the left refers to the "vulval" orgasm described by Masters and Johnson. It is referred to as "clitoral" by the Freudians because the clitoris is the common trigger point for stimulation. The most obvious manifestation of sexual response is the rhythmic contracts of the PC muscle (from *The G Spot and Other Recent Discoveries about Human Sexuality* by Alice Kahn Ladas, Beverly Whipple, and John D. Perry. © 1982 by Alice Kahn Ladas, Beverly Whipple, and Harold Ladas. Reprinted by permission of Henry Holt and Company, Inc.)

| Reference | 1 | 2 | 3 | 4 | 5 | 6 | 7 | 8 | 9 | 10 |
|---|---|---|---|---|---|---|---|---|---|---|
| Singer's categories | Vulval orgasm | | | | Blended orgasm | | | Uterine orgasm | | |
| Focus of response | PC muscle | | | | Both | | | Uterus | | |
| Common trigger point | Clitoris | | | | Several | | | G Spot | | |
| Major nerve involved | Pudendal nerve | | | | Both | | | Pelvic nerve and hypo gastric plexus | | |
| Number of orgasms | One or multiple | | | | One or multiple | | | One: Terminative | | |
| Experience focus | Orgasmic platform | | | | Vaginal | | | Uterus and pelvic organs | | |
| Male counterpart | Orgasm without semen expulsion | | | | Typical ejaculatory orgasm | | | Non-ejaculatory emission | | |
| Common names | Clitoral orgasm | | | | Vaginal orgasm | | | Vaginal orgasm | | |

Irving Singer formulated the idea of three types of orgasm. His 1973 book describes the uterine orgasm: "Subjectively the orgasm is felt to be 'deep,' i.e., dependent on repeated penis-cervix contact." This shows that the cervix is indeed involved in some orgasms.

·Uterine orgasm—involves cervical jostling
·Vulval orgasm—a clitoral climax
·Blended orgasm

The blended orgasm involves combinations of the clitoral and uterine orgasm. This means that the X-tasy Spot can be stimulated along with the G spot or the clitoris to produce orgasms.

Some women feel that the blended orgasm is superior to any other. In some cases, the clitoral orgasm may be sufficient. But in most instances, an orgasm is far better if the X-tasy Spot is stimulated.

It has been documented in a laboratory study that women can achieve orgasm through stimulation of the cervix, i.e., the X-tasy Spot. (Whipple B., Gurdes, C.A., Komisaruk, B.R., "Sexual Response to Self-Stimulation in Women with Complete Spinal Cord Injury." *The Journal of Sex Research,* Vol 33, pp. 231-240, 1996)

In the book Xaviera's Supersex, Xaviera Hollander describes what is the equivalent to the X-tasy Spot Rub: "My fingers were up against a woman's cervix. Suddenly her entire vagina swelled up like a balloon . . . like the insides of your cheeks when you blow them out." In this case, the cervix was rubbed manually for an hour resulting in a long intense orgasm. (*Xaviera's Supersex* by Xaviera Hollander, New American Library' Inc.)

To prove that the X-tasy Spot can produce strong orgasm, try the techniques in this book. Your experiences may help confirm its existence.

# Chapter 6

♥

## The Secret of Surrendering Inhibitions

Many of us were brought up to believe sex was wrong. All that was supposed to change with marriage. But for some of us, it's hard to change those views. Even though today's young adults don't have those inhibitions and many are sexually active with a number of people, they sometimes confuse quantity with quality. I would like you and your mate to have complete intimacy that lovemaking provides.

You and your man can be free from anything keeping you from experiencing ecstasy. Here's how.

# Think Back...

What was your first sexual experience? Write it down if you feel comfortable doing so.

_____

_____

_____

_____

_____

_____

_____

_____

_____

If your first sexual experience was a negative one or you have a history of abuse, find a competent counselor to help you work through any problems that negative experience may be causing. Those feelings can often block your enjoyment of the sexual experience.

What did your parents teach you about sex?

_____

_____

_____

_____

_____

_____

_____

_____

Maybe their attitude led you to believe sex is dirty. Maybe nothing was said, but even that implies a lot to a child. You need to work through some of this past negative programming to break through and live and love freely.

# Identify Your Deficiency

Before you can improve, you must know what is holding you back. Mark one of the five choices to each statement.

*I do not feel I have a right to ask my husband to meet my sexual needs.*
☐ Always ☐ Often ☐ Sometimes ☐ Rarely ☐ Never

*I fear letting go and having an orgasm.*
☐ Always ☐ Often ☐ Sometimes ☐ Rarely ☐ Never

*I think sex is for procreation, not for enjoyment.*
☐ Always ☐ Often ☐ Sometimes ☐ Rarely ☐ Never

*During lovemaking, I often wonder what my partner is thinking of my performance.*
☐ Always ☐ Often ☐ Sometimes ☐ Rarely ☐ Never

Please review your answers. Remember, everyone is different, so there are no right or wrong answers.

If you answered "Always" and "Often," you may be experiencing great difficulty asking for what pleases you during lovemaking sessions. You may have a deep seated fear of rejection.

A trained counselor can help you become more assertive in asking for what you need and become less defensive when it comes to enjoying sex.

If your answers leaned more toward the opposite end of the scale and you gave "Rarely" and "Never" replies, you are probably well-adjusted sexually.

## Self-Gratification

Masturbation is a subject much too important to be ignored. A man cannot figure out a woman's body all by himself. He needs your help because all women are different. You have to tune in to your own body to be able to teach him. Strive to understand and love yourself. Realize your own needs and accept them.

Self erotica is normal and healthy. Once you learn how to please yourself, you can teach your husband how to please you with hints and encouragement.

During foreplay, tell your partner "it feels good" if you like what he's doing. Be explicit; guide him with your hands to show him what turns you on. Women think men know instinctively what to do. This is almost never true so give your partner a little help; both of you will benefit.

## Make Noise

Inhibitions flow out of your body with each sound you make. The more you sigh and moan, the better orgasm you will have. Be a tigress in bed by making sexy animal noises. A man will usually find a growling noise in his ear quite erotic. A climax can be intensified by unleashing everything inside through screaming. It will please your husband to hear you enjoy such an overwhelming orgasm.

Getting your man to fully express his emotions may be difficult. Try a little game; tell him to make loud noises because it will "turn you on." (It will.) Make your love sounds into a contest: the loudest or wildest wins. Anything he feels should be overexaggerated. Have him breathe heavy, groan, yell, and repeat your name over and over. It will be his most sensational climax ever!

Don't explain why you are encouraging this response. It might hurt his pride if you tell him you're trying to get him to abandon his inhibitions.

## How to Talk Suggestively

Is the only way you let your man know you're in the mood to say, "Let's go to bed now," or "Let's do it"? How about spicing up your vocabulary with these phrases:

- You're my love tiger.
- I am going to seduce you tonight.
- It gets me excited when I think of you caressing my nipples.
- You make me hot.

*Now add your own suggestive "come-ons."*

_____

_____

_____

_____

_____

Here are a few words you can add to your sex vocabulary to spice it up:

| caress | horny |
|---|---|
| tantalizing | suck |
| throbbing | nibble |
| juicy | lick |

*Now write down other erotic words you can think of.*

_____  _____  _____

_____  _____  _____

_____  _____  _____

_____  _____  _____

_____  _____  _____

_____  _____  _____

"It's a funny thing about life; if you refuse to accept anything but the best, you very often get it."

–W. Somerset Maugham

# Chapter 7

♥

## Love Games

Speaker and humor consultant, Jan Marshall, founder of the International Humor Institute in Los Angeles, states that "sex and life should be fun whenever possible." She concedes that "pain, grief and disappointments occur in all humanity, but they are simply threads woven through our lives and need to be addressed and expressed. After the tears and the anguish are handled, the natural condition of life is to be joyful."

And, she claims, "sex brings much joy. Let's face it. Even mediocre sex is good. Like laughter, it relieves tension and releases endorphins, and that leads to a healthy mind/body system. If you laugh while having sex, that's even more effective. I do not mean wearing a clown nose to bed, unless, of course, that turns you on. It is simply that everybody does it, so why not have fun while we are at it. And the more you know and experiment, the more enjoyment you will manifest. In life and in bed, not a shred of evidence exists that either is serious, so just do it and do it safely. Safety is an imperative. I, myself, wear a seat belt, and I haven't fallen off the bed, yet."

# Hidden Flavor

A delicious game to be played nude. Put some flavored lip gloss, Flavored Booby Drops*, or honey somewhere on your body. Place it in a hard-to-find spot like behind your ear, the small of your back, or ankle bone. Now challenge your man to find it. He will have to lick and caress you with his tongue until he tastes it. Now it is your turn in this tantalizing game to find it on his body. If you want to keep score, time it to see who discovers the flavor in the shortest time.

# Salt Bath

Great for a terrific sauna-type effect. Beauty magazines suggest adding salt to your bath water in the interest of health. Your hubby can also join the fun. Put about three sheets and two blankets on the bed beforehand. Add at least two pounds of regular table salt to the steaming hot water. Both of you get into the bath and come out when you start feeling faint. Go directly to the bedroom and roll up in the blankets together.

Soon you will feel a warm sensation flow over your body, making your skin tingle. The two of you should start perspiring at the same time.

If you choose to make love at this time, you will experience a sensual experience as you both slide up and down on each other's wet and slippery body.

# TV Fan

A game for those avid television viewers. See who can arouse their partner the most during a commercial break and see how many commercials it takes before you shut the TV off.

## Making Bets

Instead of betting money, it's more exciting to bet the exchange of sexual favors. I mean this in a very lighthearted way. Make a bet and whoever wins gets his or her favorite sexual position or the lucky winner receives a special night to be pampered and make the lovemaking decisions. You may like to bet a half-hour body massage with hot oils* and the works.

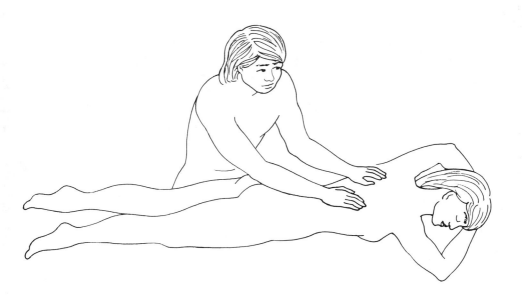

## Pop Rocks

This game involves oral sex, a variation of making love, so if you feel an aversion for it, you can skip this one. Buy exploding candy and put it in your mouth before performing fellatio on your man. Your surprised husband will hear fireworks as the candy cracks and pops in your mouth. He will also feel a pleasant sensation from this sizzling candy.

You can use hot tea, mint toothpaste, whipped cream*, ice, or honey instead. Wrapping your man's penis in a sheet of dried roll-up fruit* is fun and tastes good, too.

# Down and Dirty Mud Wrestling[1]

If you don't mind getting messy, mix several boxes of instant chocolate pudding and two gallons of milk in a clean bathtub. When your sweetie comes home, be in your swimming suit (or naked) and ask him if he'd like to mud wrestle. The clean up is tasty and fun.

# Sexy Wake-up Alarm

Get a tape recorder and a blank tape and turn it on when the two of you get turned on. Be very explicit — say everything that is happening and the way it feels; for example:

- I love it when you lick my stomach and caress my nipples.
- I feel my nipples getting hard as you lightly lick them.
- I'm getting hot, and I feel your hard penis throbbing against my body.

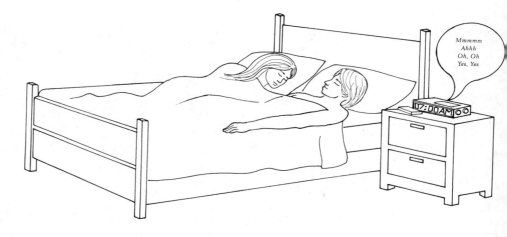

As you make love, record the love noises of your climax together. In the morning, set your alarm at least 10 minutes earlier, rewind the tape, and turn it on. When your man hears your orgasm on tape, he will really wake up.

# Flash Cards

Decide in the morning to make up six flash cards each telling your lover to perform some sexual act for you. Do not tell each other what you are writing. That evening at bedtime, instead of talking, take turns showing your flash cards and acting them out for three minutes each. No talking, but moaning and groaning is allowed!

# Guessing Game

Blindfold your partner and then touch him with different objects. He has to guess correctly before going on. Touch his back and all parts of his naked body with various items, like a feather duster, hairbrush, cucumber, silk scarf, magazine, and so on. He can do the same for you if he likes.

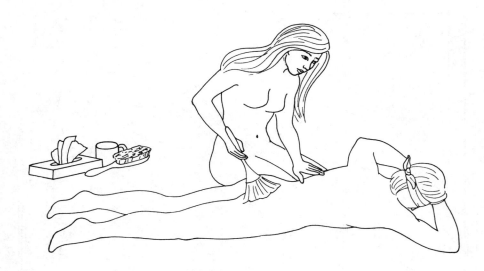

# The Freeze[2]

*(Play this game during lovemaking.)* There are two ways to play The Freeze. The first is to set a timer, or several timers, in advance. The second is to assign one of the partners the role of alarm clock. When the timer goes off or the alarm clock partner calls *time*, both freeze. Stop completely. Do not move. Simply lie still and be aware of the continued motion of your sensations, thoughts, and emotions. The main thing is not to move in the slightest. Don't move for at least one minute. When you continue, everything will be more intense. You can do this once or many times while making love.

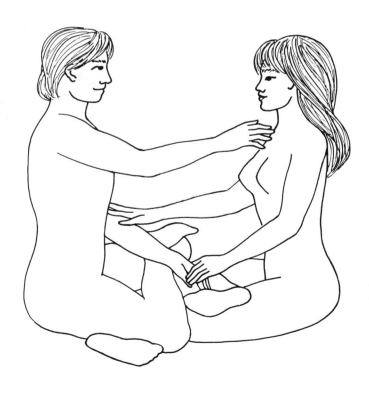

# Human Greeting Card

Use body paint* to write a message across your nude body. Write "Happy Birthday" or "Happy Anniversary, Honey!" or write directions on your body like, "Start Here," "Go Here Next," "Stop," "Go On," and use arrows to direct him. He'll get the hint.

# Fantasy Game

Tell your partner about a wild sexual escapade you experienced together; an imaginary situation that can only happen in your dreams. Create the circumstances as you go along. The tale you spin can be something like this:

> We met at work. Our first assignment together was painting a water tower. It was a sizzling hot day. As we reached the top of the tower, I looked up and saw your broad shoulders glistening with sweat. I tore off my blouse and you pulled off your jeans and we started going at it on top of the water tower, etc...

Now your partner has to top that story with one he makes up. (Fun to play on long, boring drives.)

# Dirty Dice

Use a special pair of dice*. One die has words of things to do to each other, like *nibble, suck,* or *lick.* The other die has the different parts of the body to do it to, such as *nipple, toe,* or *crotch.* Roll the dice together and then act out the directions.

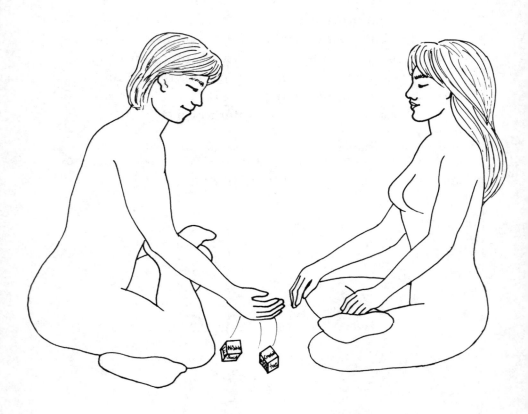

# Water Games

There are lots of games you can play in the bath or shower. Here are just a few examples:

- Buy some colored soap crayons (sold for children's bath time) and use them to color your lover.
- Spray crazy soap foam all over each other's body and rub-a-dub-dub.
- Use the water stream from the faucet or a shower massage attachment to give each other a climax in the tub.

# Alien Fantasy

Pretend your partner is an alien from space and you want to have sex but he doesn't know how. You have to take him by the hand and teach him everything since he has no previous knowledge. Next time, you be the alien, and he will show you what turns him on.

# Love Hunt

If you have to be away from home without him, hide a note somewhere like on top of the refrigerator that says, "I love you — go to plant in living room." Tape a message (out of sight) on the plant that states, "I miss you — go to bathroom medicine chest." Have a note hidden behind a bottle that warns, "You are HOT! — Go to bedroom and look under the bed." Have a present waiting there for him with a letter from you. Then just call him up on the phone and say, "Honey, when you get a chance, look on top of the fridge. I left a note for you."

1. from *A Woman's Little Black Book of Romantically Crazy Ideas,* by Heidi Larsen, p. 73 *(ISBN: 1-56684-007-4).*

2. from *Sexual Energy Ecstasy, A Practical Guide to Lovemaking Secrets of the East and West,* by David and Ellen Ramsdale, pp. 214-215.

I would like to credit my good friend Carol Tracey with the suggestions for TV Fan and Flash Card games.

I wish I could make up 101 Love Games, but try as I might, I can't, but I'll bet you're creative enough to invent at least four new ones. Give it your best shot. If you come up with a dozen love games, write to me so that I can consult with you on my next book.

## Love Games

_____

_____

_____

_____

_____

_____

_____

_____

_____

_____

# Chapter 8

♥

## 101 Erotic Things to Do to Your Man

This list of 101 Erotic Things to Do is just the beginning. You and your spouse have the rest of your lives together to experiment and delight each other with unusual erotic things.

1. Lick his belly button (men usually love it or hate it).
2. Write him a sexy note.
3. Buy him a bouquet of flowers.
4. Give him a coupon for one "free, no obligation" climax.
5. Rub his feet, especially the sensitive part between his toes (rarely ever touched).
6. Let him know (while at a restaurant or other public place) that you are wearing crotchless panties*.
7. Give him a French manicure or a facial.
8. Kiss, suck, and nibble on his nipples.
9. Each of you put a different flavor lifesaver in your mouth, then exchange flavors (no hands).
10. Buy shaving lather that gets hot and blindfold him or have him close his eyes, and apply it all over his body.

11. Around Halloween buy a glow lipstick (under $2.00 at the drug store). Write a message on your body, turn off the lights, and turn on your man. It's fun to color certain private parts of your body and make heart shapes, etc.

12. Wear only a hat and gloves or sunglasses and boots while making love.

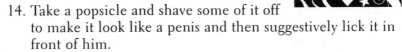

13. Take your finger (palm upward) and lightly rub the ridges on the roof of his mouth.

14. Take a popsicle and shave some of it off to make it look like a penis and then suggestively lick it in front of him.

15. You can buy plastic sheets for under $10.00; then use a couple of bottles of oil* and really slip around. Or use a plastic drop cloth for painting (around $2.00) to protect the sheets.

16. Cover the bed with rose petals for a romantic evening.

17. Light as many candles as you can for a warm glow.

18. Make love in a car (even if it's parked in your own driveway).

19. For an exotic mood, light incense.

20. Wear a white T-shirt while you shower together.

21. Make love in front of a mirror.

22. Right before your lover climaxes, put ice on his sensitive parts.

23. Make love on the kitchen counter, dining room table, or on the washing machine during the spin cycle.

24. Buy him a sexy tuxedo brief to wear.

25. Make sure he owns one pair of silk or fishnet underwear.

26. Inflate a lot of balloons and place them in the bedroom with messages written on them, like "World's Greatest Lover" and/or kiss an inflated balloon after putting red lipstick on. When you deflate the balloon, it will have tiny lip prints all over it.

27. Add a hard boiled egg to his lunch with "I love you — can't wait until you get home," written on it.

28. Write "I love you" in the sand or snow.

29. Buy one of those fabric marking pens with disappearing ink and write "Let's make love" boldly across a T-shirt just before he comes home from work.

30. Use three vibrators* at once.

31. Buy a black-light bulb for the night stand lamp. The light will make you look like you have a dark tan and anything white will glow a bright purple.

32. Make love looking out a window, or go down on him (back against the wall on your knees) while he is standing in front of a window looking out.

33. Figure out 101 different ways to kiss.

34. Pinch his rear-end unexpectedly.

35. Fake an orgasm in his ear during a commercial.

36. Turn off all lights in the bed-room, then turn on a small flashlight and shine it on his private parts as you kiss and caress him there.

37. Wake him up by going down on him.

38. Late one summer evening, make love on the roof or, if that is out of the question, at least make love in the backyard.

39. Give his penis a pet name.

40. Make love hanging from the ceiling in a Taiwan basket.

41. Around Christmas, put a string of lights around your naked body. In a darkened room wait for him to enter and then plug them in. (Make sure you have the new fire- and shock-proof ones.)

42. Eat a juicy peach or plum together; one person biting from one side as the other bites the other side simulta-neously.

43. Brush your hair up and down his naked body.

44. Write a message on the bathroom mirror with a little shaving cream, then carefully wipe it off. When he goes in the bathroom to shower and shave, the mirror will steam up everywhere but the place you had the shaving cream, and reveal your message.

45. Ask him to remove your panties with his teeth.

46. Remove his briefs with your teeth.

47. Flutter your eyelashes on his cheek.

48. Kiss him and say "I love you" 50 times.

49. Take pictures in the bedroom with a Polaroid camera for pictures just the two of you will see.

50. Wear edible underwear*.

51. Lick his eyelashes.

52. Write "I love you" in several different languages.

53. Blow in his ear and simultaneously rub the small of his back with your palm. (It gives some men an instant erection.)

54. Give him lots of celery to eat so when you go down on him, his semen will taste sweeter.

55. Instead of throwing out an old bra, wear it one last time when you know you're going to make love. As your husband starts caressing you and removes your blouse, tell him to rip the bra off—that you can't wait.

56. Write a short romance story for him to read.

57. Gather up some silk scarves and rub them all over his body.

58. Give him a gift certificate for a professional massage on a special occasion.

59. Join the mile-high club (make love in an airplane).

60. Tickle each other with feathers.

61. Use a blindfold*. You can't see what he is going to do next, so you anticipate where the next caress or kiss will be. You become more aware and more turned on.

62. When camping, make love in the sleeping bag in a tent.

63. Make love outside in the rain. On a warm night, the sensation of the rain drops hitting naked bodies feels erotic.

64. Wear a pair of clip-on earrings on your nipples.

65. Put body glitter* on your body before doing a sexy dance.

66. Engrave a sexy message on the inside of his leather belt.

67. Find his G spot!

68. Wear a figure enhancing push-up bra.

69. Spray a can of whipped cream* on each other's body and lick it off.

70. Wear a wig. Behave out of character, like a totally different   person.

71. Trim each other's pubic hair.

72. Send flowers to his mom on his birthday. Say, "Thanks for raising such a fine young man."

73. Take gelatin tablets and pretend they're aphrodisiacs—go wild on each other.

74. Play a game of strip poker.

75. Play "For Lovers Only"* game; it's a full-size board game.

76. Rub fur on each other's bodies or lie on a real fur rug.

77. Go for a walk in the moonlight—kiss in the moonlight.

78. Drop a trail of sexy underwear leading to the bedroom.

79. Make love on a hammock. He can lie down on it and you can sit facing him. Your feet will touch the ground, giving you great leverage and freedom of movement.

80. Make love in various positions with a bright light shining on you so you make shadow pictures on the wall.

81. Go somewhere formal and tell him you forgot to wear panties.

82. Blindfold your man and caress his penis with your hands until he gets hard. Then put a facial mask cream on his penis while you tell him stories or rub other parts of his body. Use the kind of mask that feels tingly and dries tight.

While it is drying, your man won't know what is going on. After it's dry, wipe it off with a warm wash cloth and make love to him.

83. One evening while he's soaking in the tub, walk into the bathroom to bring him extra towels. Then jump into the tub (clothes and all) and start kissing him.

84. If he works in the garage, walk in to tell him dinner is ready, then take off your coat and have nothing on under it.

85 .Make up a secret code name for making love or certain initials that mean it.

86. Call him on the phone to tell him how much he turns you on.

87. Put a menthol rub all over each other's body. The sensation is that of intense hot and cold, almost like pain and pleasure. Do not put it on your genitals—it will burn.

88. Have your husband stand behind you as you both face a mirror with your back against his stomach. Reach behind yourself to take his hands in yours. Place his hands over your breasts and guide his hands with just the right pressure and movement for what feels good to you. Slowly move his hands down your belly, all the while keeping your hands on top of his. Push on his fingers so he rubs you between your legs with just the right stroke. Help him bring you to climax, then switch roles.

89. On Valentine's Day, put an ad in the "Personals" in the newspaper telling him that you love him.

90. While celebrating, save some champagne to pour onto each other's naked bodies and lick it off. Or dip his penis in a glass of champagne.

91. Buy flavored Emotion Lotion*. Pour some on his back and rub it so it gets warm. When you blow on it, it gets hot. It may be used as a lubricant also.

92. Cut out heart shapes from dried roll-up fruit you buy at the supermarket. When you wet them, they will stick to your body like a fun, edible tattoo.

93. Buy matching pajamas for the two of you.

94. Take a long, luxurious bubble bath together.

95. Lick his ear, then gently inhale— evaporation of moisture feels better than just blowing in your man's ear.

96. Spend time together relaxing in a hot tub, jacuzzi, or whirlpool.

97. Cup your breast in your hand and rub your nipple across your husband's face, chest, stomach and legs. Use nothing but your nipple to caress him all over.

98. Turn on a strobe light and do a wild striptease for your hubby. The light makes everything look slow motion.

99. When shopping with your mate at a mall, stop at one of those instant photo booths. Tell him to stand guard in front of the door with the curtain. Once in there, unbutton your blouse, pull it open and give your sexiest centerfold look. Boy, will he be surprised at what develops.

100. After taking a shower together, use the feather applicator to apply edible Honey Dust* to your lover's body. Then, like the sex kitten you are, slowly lick it off.

101. It seems these 50s style diners are popping up everywhere. Sometimes they have a machine that will make a medallion for 50¢. You get to choose the letters to put on it. You can make one up for your sweetie that says your name and his, forever. Or make a token that says "Good for one free orgasm." Won't that be fun to trade back and forth?

# Erotic Things to Do

Write down some of the novel things you've done in the past, and invent some new ones to do in the future.

_____

_____

_____

_____

_____

_____

_____

_____

_____

_____

_____

_____

_____

_____

_____

_____

_____

_____

# Chapter 9

## Fantasies

Acting out a fantasy is like exploring a new sexual frontier. It builds anticipation with a strong sense of adventure. Fantasies can put the fire back into your marriage.

The kind of fantasy you select is a personal choice you must decide with your spouse. Remember, anything pleasurable to both partners, practiced in privacy, is good for a marriage. Make up things to do and agree about them ahead of time.

As with other fantasies, role playing can help you gain insight into your relationship. Invent roles that are suitable for the two of you. Be creative and you will find that the potential for making up new fantasy love games is unlimited.

Attitude and creativity are all-important. Some say ALL sex is in your head. That's true up to a point.

If you find you do not know where to begin creating a fantasy, try sharing honest and open communication with your lover. If either of you find it difficult to talk openly about sex, write out a script. Write your fantasy into a play for both of you to act out. It will take courage and perhaps some persuasion, but it will be worth the effort. Your husband will find it fascinating to be the main star in a play you wrote just for him.

Open the door to fantasies and reawaken your innermost longings. Keep these lover's games special by indulging in them only occasionally. Once a month should keep the spark in any relationship.

Trying and practicing these techniques within the framework of marriage improves your relationship with each other. Your marriage has a foundation of love and respect to begin with. Add the commitment and trust developed in acting out your innermost thoughts, and you will have an intimacy with each other you can have with no one else.

Joseph Fetterman states, "Sex is a flame which uncontrolled may scorch; properly guided, it will light the torch of eternity."

One word of caution: some fantasies are better left as fantasies. It is fun to be naughty and daring in the bedroom, but use discretion. Do not let real people you know enter your fantasy. Pretending a friend or acquaintance is a character in the fantasy could inject hurt or jealousy into the game. You have each other so there is no need for anyone else. You might, instead, pretend you and your mate have just met. Get to know each other all over again.

An exciting scene is pretending you are a twin sister of yourself. Try to seduce your man while he resists giving in to his desires because he is already married to your sister. It gives you a chance to take the initiative and play the dominant role.

Another possibility is to exchange roles with your husband for an evening. He might cook dinner, or you might take him out to a restaurant. Make love during the role reversal.

Your husband may fancy himself James Bond 007 and you a beautiful Russian agent seducing him while on a secret mission. To make your fantasies more believable, you might even try dressing up in the costumes of your story.

# Chapter 10

♥

## The Sex Exercise

This is an amazingly simple exercise that can increase your pleasure tenfold when making love.

While lying down or standing up, do the following simultaneously *(see illustrations on next page)*:

- If lying down, bring your knees up, keep your feet flat on the floor and lift your hips off the floor.
- If standing, bring your arms and shoulders forward and bend your knees.
- Tighten your buttocks' cheeks hard and pull them in close to each other.
- Pull in your stomach as hard as you can. Use all your strength to hold the abdominal muscles tight, suck your tummy in till you start to quiver and shake.
- Contract your inner bladder muscles as if you have the strong urge to urinate and can't right away.
- Hold for one minute. Then relax your whole body. Repeat the exercise 12 times. Work up to 60 repetitions.

## Lying Down

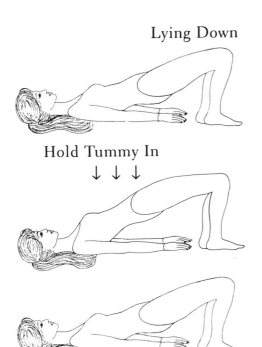

**Hold Tummy In**
↓  ↓  ↓

## Standing Up

Hold
Tummy →
In →

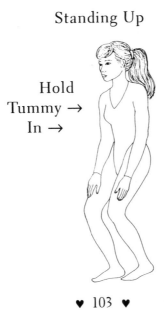

Perform this sex exercise once or twice a day for dramatic results. Test your inner muscles to chart your progress. When you are in the washroom, try to stop the flow of urine once you start. Practice until you can.

Also, this exercise will flatten your stomach. Your buttocks will also become firmer and improve your body's appearance. A bonus of the exercise is that you will look slimmer and feel more self-confident. You will literally lose inches around the middle part of your body.

Check your progress by taking your measurements periodically. Use the chart below to keep track.

### First Day before Doing the Exercise

Date: _____

Waist Measurement: _____

Hip Measurement: _____

Buttocks Measurement: _____

### One Week after Doing the Exercise

Date: _____

Waist Measurement: _____

Hip Measurement: _____

Buttocks Measurement: _____

*Front View*

Waist Measurement
Hip Measurement
Buttocks Measurement

### Two Weeks after Doing the Exercise

Date: _____

Waist Measurement: _____

Hip Measurement: _____

Buttocks Measurement: _____

### Three Weeks after Doing the Exercise

Date: _____

Waist Measurement: _____

Hip Measurement: _____

Buttocks Measurement: _____

### One Month after Doing the Exercise

Date: _____

Waist Measurement: _____

Hip Measurement: _____

Buttocks Measurement: _____

*SideView*

Waist measurement

Hip Measurement

Buttocks Measurement

While increasing your sexual pleasure, this simple exercise can improve your husband's enjoyment as well. He'll tell you how much tighter you feel when making love. You will have more control over your body and will probably reach orgasm sooner. The alternate squeezing and relaxing of the inside muscles will bring both of you more satisfaction.

## Making the Sex Exercise More Effective

Using Ben Wa Balls* (like using weights for your arms) increases the effectiveness of the Sex Exercise one-hundred percent. Every woman should have her own set of gold Ben Wa Balls. They look like two gold marbles, the diameter of a nickel.

*Actual size of Ben Wa Balls*

It is said that in China women use Ben Wa Balls to masturbate. They put the gold balls inside the vagina and then rock back and forth. They say the pleasurable sensations give them one climax after another.

In America, women use the balls for exercise. If a woman wanted to increase the size and strength of her arm muscle, isometric exercise would help. But lifting a 20 pound weight would be better.

At first, it's a good idea to start out wearing only one ball to get used to it. When you are ready to use both, do not wear crotchless panties and a skirt because the first time you sneeze, you'll send those babies flying! Wear panties and jeans; then, if you laugh and they come out, it will be as if you laid a golden egg, but at least they won't roll away. You can wear them all the time, around the house, grocery shopping, and to work. Just don't wear them when you go through a metal detector at the airport, because they will set it off.

A model puts a book on her head and walks around her apartment to improve her posture and balance. At first it is a conscious effort, but after awhile, her posture improves. She stands up straight whether the book is placed upon her head or not. So it is with the Ben Wa Balls. At first you will consciously hold them in by taking small steps and holding your stomach in, but after a while, your pubococcygeus muscles will strengthen and you will automatically be able to hold the balls inside effortlessly.

> *Caution: Do not leave the Ben Wa Balls in while making love. Also, remove them before going to the washroom. After use, wash them with soap and water.*

Strengthen your muscles not only for your man (even though he will find the milking sensation very pleasurable) but for yourself as well. When a woman has a climax, her muscles involuntarily contract and release, so if she learns to do it earlier in lovemaking, she will have a climax sooner and that climax will be more intense. Also, it will be easy to bring your man to climax without even moving your body. Contracting and releasing the "love muscle" is all it will take to bring your man to incredible heights.

Practicing this technique results in strengthening the vaginal muscles so you will be able to hold the man's penis inside you even though he tries to withdraw it. It is a rare and unique woman who knows this secret.

# Chapter 11

♥

## Prolonging Your Man's Pleasure

Some men have problems maintaining an erection or may ejaculate prematurely. Sex therapists sometimes advise couples with premature ejaculation difficulties to have extended sessions of foreplay. This helps the man get comfortable with the idea of staying hard, but not having to perform. The foreplay should consist of fondling his penis slowly for a long time. Make sure he has an erection, but do not bring him to a climax.

Help your man practice maintaining an erection three times a week. On alternate days, have intercourse. During sex, if you sense your man is nearing climax too soon, press firmly with two or three fingers on his urethra near the root of the penis to prevent ejaculation. Press hard, but not so hard as to bruise, or press midway between the scrotum and the rectum.

If your man has the problem of premature ejaculation, always be understanding. Never get angry although at times you may feel frustrated. If you comment on how unsatisfactory it was, you may do irreparable damage. Show him instead how to satisfy you with his hands and mouth.

Some tips on prolonging the sex act:

- Have sex more often.

- The second consecutive time you make love, the man will last longer.

- Try taking the upper position and doing all the moving while he lies still.

- Have your husband wear a condom or try an anesthetic jelly, such as Prolong Creme*, on his penis to reduce sensitivity.

- Before he climaxes, change positions or have him withdraw and rest (he can keep you stimulated using his fingers).

- He can think of things irrelevant to the act of making love. Some men figure out mathematical problems in their head.

- Eastern people have a remedy for the man who is tired or has a premature ejaculation. They employ the sex exercise technique. In this technique, you arouse your husband, then, when his penis is hard, have him put it inside you.

  Instead of moving, stay still. He should move only if it is necessary to maintain the erection. After quite a while, your muscles will automatically start contracting, enabling you to have orgasm after orgasm without wearing your man out.

- He can use a cock ring*. This is an adjustable leather band that fits around the base of the man's testicles and penis. A soft leather ring is safe because it is removable at any time by unsnapping it.

  Once your man has a climax with it on, leave it on and help him get hard again. This time it will take him three times longer to come. If he normally stays hard for five minutes, it will take him 15 minutes to ejaculate. Remove the ring after the second ejaculation (see diagram on next page).

As a precaution, ask your doctor first about any dangers associated with its use.

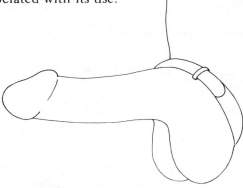

- Your husband can purposely slow his breathing down. In addition, he can relax the tenseness in his leg and foot muscles. Some men have to stiffen their legs and point their toes during climax.

If after trying these remedies your husband is still having trouble, he should consult a doctor. Be aware that some medicines cause impotence.

# Chapter 12

♥

## Woman as a Sexual Being in
## the Marriage Relationship

Much has been written about the role that the man should play in the sexual experience. The man is portrayed as the master of the situation. Usually, the man must feel that he is in control. Because of this, it is he who feels inadequate if he cannot bring his partner to orgasm. He feels shame at less than Olympic performance. She feels bored. This is a picture that was perpetuated up until recently.

Great sex takes work — your work, his work. Sisters, we have some catching up to do! Not only work — great sex takes time. My friend, the Rev. William Fontaine, advises, "The best way to keep the romance alive is to make time for it."

The average orgasm lasts for only TEN SECONDS! After experiencing the X-tasy Spot rub, you will have a longer orgasm in just one night than most women experience in three years!

There are 24 hours in a day. How will you choose to use your time? With just work, sleep, hobbies and TV? The national average per day for television watching is more than SIX HOURS!

# What is Your Priority

Make a list of excuses why you don't put your "all" into lovemaking sessions.

*For example:*

> No time.
> Kids home.
> Too tired.
> Work too late.
> It takes too much effort.
> Why bother?
> I don't feel attractive.

*Add your own excuses:*

_____

_____

_____

_____

_____

_____

_____

_____

_____

_____

# Why Change?

Now think of the consequences of not putting effort into your lovemaking:

> Familiarity breeds contempt.
>
> I am not sexually satisfied.
>
> My husband is not satisfied.
>
> He or I might start looking for another person to meet this need and therefore jeopardize our home.
>
> My husband does not consider me exciting.
>
> I do not feel sexy.

*Now add your own consequences:*

_____

_____

_____

_____

_____

_____

_____

_____

_____

_____

# Benefits of Changing

Now make another list of the benefits of making sex more interesting:

I will feel more confident.

All that sex will burn calories and help me lose weight.

My husband will find me exciting.

No more routine sex.

I will know I am a great lover.

I will feel less jealous of other women.

My man will appreciate the fact I am willing to put effort into our lovemaking.

My husband will be sexually satisfied.

I will keep him guessing as to what erotic things I might do next.

My body will feel more healthy and alive.

I will feel less tension.

I will experience the warm, radiant feeling you get after making love more often.

*My benefits are:*

_____

_____

_____

_____

_____

*More benefits:*

_____

_____

_____

_____

_____

_____

_____

_____

_____

_____

_____

_____

_____

_____

_____

_____

_____

_____

_____

_____

_____

_____

_____

_____

*Weigh the Pros and Cons:*

_____

_____

_____

_____

_____

_____

_____

_____

_____

_____

_____

_____

_____

_____

_____

_____

_____

_____

_____

_____

_____

_____

_____

# Love Styles Test

1. Do you love long dinners at cozy restaurants?
   ❑ yes ❑ no

2. Are you embarrassed to talk about sex?
   ❑ yes ❑ no

3. Does loud music with a strong beat stimulate you?
   ❑ yes ❑ no

4. Do you wear little or no makeup?
   ❑ yes ❑ no

5. Is your idea of a two-day dream vacation with your man (*choose one*):
   ❑ a. an island of your own
   ❑ b. city lights, best restaurants, and dance club
   ❑ c. the majestic mountains
   ❑ d. a cottage with a fragrant flower garden

6. Do you like your man to be the strong, rugged type?
   ❑ yes ❑ no

7. Is it very important to you that your husband shows he loves you by sending roses and cards?
   ❑ yes ❑ no

8. Does a "lady" by day, "whore" by night mentality offend you?
   ❑ yes ❑ no

9. Do you ask your husband for permission to buy something you really want?
   ❑ yes ❑ no

10. Do you feel most intimate with your lover *(choose one)*:
 ☐ a. snuggling up on the couch together
 ☐ b. after a fabulous party
 ☐ c. when he whispers "I love you" in your ear
 ☐ d. holding hands while on a long walk together

11. Do you think some things are erotic that others consider kinky?
 ☐ yes ☐ no

12. Do you dream about being swept away by the perfect man?
 ☐ yes ☐ no

13. There is nothing more romantic than being together looking at *(choose one)*:
 ☐ a. the city skyline twinkling at night
 ☐ b. a beautiful sunset
 ☐ c. the snow-capped mountains
 ☐ d. a beautiful, fragrant flower garden

14. Does nature inspire you?
 ☐ yes ☐ no

15. Do you pout when you don't get your way?
 ☐ yes ☐ no

16. Is your perfume a floral scent?
 ☐ yes ☐ no

17. Do you like luxurious bath crystals?
 ☐ yes ☐ no

18. Have you ever made explicit sexual demands of your husband?
 ☐ yes ☐ no

## *Key*

1. yes = c
2. yes = a
3. yes = b
4. yes = d
5. a = c
   b = b
   c = d
   d = a
6. yes = d & a
7. yes = c
8. yes = a, c, & d
9. yes = a
10. a = a & c
    b = b
    c = c & a
    d = d

11. yes = b
12. yes = c
13. a = b
    b = d & c
    c = c & d
    d = a
14. yes = d
15. yes = a
16. yes = d & a
17. yes = c
18. yes = b

## Directions

Now go back over the answers you gave on the test. Look at the corresponding number on the key and if you answered *yes* and the key states *yes=c*, score yourself with the letter *c*. If you answered *yes* and the key states that *yes=a*, score yourself with the letter *a*. Then total each of the letters *a*, *b*, *c*, and *d*.

*Total for a =* _____
*Total for b =* _____
*Total for c =* _____
*Total for d =* _____

# — What is Your Love Style —
# — What is Your Personality Type —
# — What Lingerie Complements You? —

If you got six to 10 *a* answers, you are:

- Shy, coy, and suggestive — sometimes acting like a little girl. You probably wear "baby dolls" and cotton lingerie in pastel colors.

If you got four to seven *b* answers, you are:

- Strong, dominant, and aggressive — you know what kind of sex you want and you go after it. You make explicit, bold statements. You probably wear tiger print or black, maybe a bustier with fishnet hose and high heels.

If you got four to seven *c* answers, you are:

- Romantic, warm, and loving — you love holding hands, slow dancing, and candles. You love being seduced by your husband. You may like a long, flowing gown, or lots of ruffles and lace lingerie that is very feminine.

If you got five to eight *d* answers, you are:

- Country fresh and outdoorsy — you love picnics and long walks together in the woods. You may like classic cami tap pants sets in a floral print.

# What Does Sexual Satisfaction Mean to You?

Examples:

- Hour-long orgasms?
- Having any orgasm at all?
- Pleasing your partner?
- Looking like a sex goddess with the perfect body of a 20-year old? *(For some people this one is a little unrealistic and we can't make it happen, although I would suggest trying a little self-acceptance instead.)*

*Your own answers:*

_____

_____

_____

_____

_____

_____

_____

_____

_____

_____

_____

_____

*Look over your list from the previous page.*

Are there any unrealistic answers?
☐ yes ☐ no

Any impossible ones?
☐ yes ☐ no

Could you be setting yourself up to be disappointed?
☐ yes ☐ no

Do you have answers that are easy to achieve?
☐ yes ☐ no

Are you sexually satisfied?
☐ yes ☐ no

If you have any unrealistic goals, can you change them into something easily attainable?
☐ yes ☐ no

I hope these questions helped you gain new insight about your feelings on sexual satisfaction.

# Suggestions

At first blush, "machismo" between the sheets looks great. The woman faces no demands. The man gets to be in the saddle.

It doesn't have to be that way. Now, in sex, too, you can take charge of your destiny. Create pleasure for yourself. Control more than you ever imagined. Expand your role, become more active. Master your body. Mastering the X-tasy Spot techniques teaches you that you are the master of your body.

An orgasm is not something a man gives a woman. It is not like presenting her with a diamond ring that she happily receives. A woman has her own orgasm. Of course, a man can help it happen, but it is still her orgasm. She must release all her inhibitions.

It is her responsibility to teach him and let him know what causes her to orgasm. There are many ways to do this; tell him, direct his hand, and read parts of this book together. Communicate what feels good and what takes you toward your goal or orgasm.

Many parts of this book refer to getting to know yourself and learn your own body. This is very important because every woman is different and your man is not a mind reader.

A load is being lifted from you and your lover. He becomes less pressured to perform. You must learn new ways so both of you can be free to enjoy making love.

The suggestions on the following pages are only suggestions. It is up to you to carry them out. You will discover that, if you do, your spouse will become ever more responsive to you.

1. Don't demand anything from your spouse. If you demand sex, it will become a chore. If it becomes a chore, he will become resentful. Resentment breeds impotence. Impotence breeds broader conflicts. These conflicts could have been avoided simply by a slight change in your attitude.

It is never necessary to demand anything. It is always more desirable to ask your spouse if he would like to make love. If he refuses, ask him if there is anything on his mind. This will allow him to vent anything that is bothering him. When he does this, listen to him. This is important. If he feels that he is being heard, he'll feel closer to you. This, in turn, will make it far more likely that he will want to make love to you.

2. Consider doing whatever he likes. This is extremely important. This may seem like a tall order if he happens to like some activities that you do not enjoy or that you find kinky. But it's important to realize that there is very little in sex that is actually kinky. If he likes things that you consider kinky, you need to talk out the problem instead of acting it out.

3. Do whatever you like. The same rule applies to you that applies to your spouse. A woman has an enormous inborn capacity to experience sexual pleasure. This inborn capacity is not something to be wasted. God gave us this capacity. It is to be enjoyed, and it is to be enjoyed to its fullest. Our capacity for joy is also inborn.

Our capacity for sexual pleasure, like our capacity for joy, is inborn. Yet people who would not question our right to experience joy question our right to experience sexual pleasure. Surely, if we have the right to have joy in our lives, we also have the right to enjoy sex.

The capacity for sexual pleasure is not only inborn — we are capable of enhancing it. Sexual fulfillment in our marriage is an expression of God's will. Therefore, we should be thankful that we have such a joyous manner in which to express God's will.

*There are several things that you can do to enhance what you have learned. Here are some tips:*

1. Don't force yourself to do anything that is painful. If you experience pain, that is your body's way of telling you to stop.

2. Don't force yourself to do anything that you find repulsive. It's your right to say no.

3. If you normally are able to do something but you feel too tired or not in the mood to do it, don't feel obliged to do it at that time.

4. If you are normally able to do something but you are having a problem with your spouse in the nonsexual sphere, don't use sex as a means of trying to solve or cure that problem. Every problem must be solved on its own level and cannot be solved magically by resorting to pleasure. There is a place for pleasure, and that place is in enhancing a relationship.

5. If you desire another person, you should ask yourself why. If your desire is simply an expression of a natural attraction, this does not mean that you should act on that desire. You shouldn't. If your desire is a result of a problem in your relationship, it is even more important not to act on that desire. A problem must be solved on its own level and will not be cured magically through pleasure. The more you are able to confront a problem, the stronger you will become. As you become stronger, your sexual relationship will become better.

6. Your sexual relationship is the expression of many factors. If you doubt this, try a little experiment. Attempt to have sex when you are having a problem or are too tired, angry, or upset with your spouse. You will experience difficulty enjoying sex.

7. Remember that you are in charge of your sexual capacity. This means that you have the ability to enjoy it to the fullest, to develop it so that you will enjoy it to the fullest, and to take responsibility for pleasing yourself and your partner.

If you find that you are having problems in either the sexual or the nonsexual aspect of the relationship, and the advice given here does not result in an improvement in either aspect, don't hesitate to consult someone. This can be a minister, priest, rabbi, counselor, or some other professional who is trained to listen to you.

There is enough information here to equip every woman to get more enjoyment from her sex life. The information is both theoretical and practical. You need both. The theory has presented a view of female sexuality as multifaceted because every woman is unique.

A wealth of information is available on the techniques for achieving a fulfilling sexual relationship. Now is the time to recognize that the rest is up to you. You now have the knowledge, the skills, and the wisdom to attain maximum pleasure. If this is not enough, you may have some other problem that you need to examine or discuss.

You now also have some good insights into the way that sex fits into your relationship. If you have a good relationship to begin with, the chances are that your sex life also will be good. If you have a good sex life to begin with, the chances also are good that your relationship is in good shape. The two complement each other.

You need to put into practice what you have learned in this book. But you also need to realize that what you do is a matter of preference. If you prefer to use the G spot, this is what you should do. If, on the other hand, you prefer to use the clitoris, that is what you should do. Remember that there are no "shoulds" in sex. Do not feel inadequate or guilty if you fail to achieve an orgasm by some means that has been hailed by a writer. You are the best judge of what practice to employ. That is your privilege. It is, after all, your body.

# Intimacy Test:
# How Well Do You
# Know Your Man?

1. What is his favorite color?

2. What is his favorite song?

3. What is his worst fear?

4. What makes him the happiest?

5. What does your husband need most from you?

6. What is his favorite drink?

7. What is his favorite way to relax?

8. What is his favorite sex position?

9. What is his favorite book?

10. What kind of lingerie does he like to see you in?

11. What is his sexual fantasy?

12. What was his first sexual experience?

13. What were his parents' attitude toward sex?

_____

14. Who does he most admire?

_____


When you take the time to really get to know your man, it will foster his feelings of being understood and cared about. He, in turn, will show more love and understanding toward you.

Please remember, this is not a test. It is added to this manual to get you thinking about intimacy, and if you find you can't answer half of these questions, maybe you need to get to know your husband better by asking him these questions and then really listening to his answers. Ask him how he feels about all these things.

# Sexuality Questionnaire

The information obtained from this questionnaire may be used in my next book. Please mail to:

Debbie Tideman, PO Box 388067, Chicago, IL 60638

1. Are you married?  ☐ yes ☐ no
2. How long have you been married?
3. How old are you?
4. How many times do you make love per month?
5. How often do you have an orgasm while making love?
   ☐ never  ☐ rarely  ☐ usually  ☐ always
6. How often do you have a climax during foreplay (i.e. manual stimulation of the clitoris)?
   ☐ never  ☐ rarely  ☐ usually  ☐ always
7. Where is the most exotic or unusual place you've made love?
8. Does your lover know where your G spot is?
   ☐ yes ☐ no
9. Sexually speaking, if you were to wave a magic wand and he would change, what is it about your partner you would like to see changed?

_____

_____

_____

_____

_____

10. If you and your partner ever made up any original love games, could you please describe them?

_____

_____

_____

_____

11. What questions would you like to see answered in my next book?

_____

_____

_____

_____

12. What area of sexuality would you like to learn more about?

_____

_____

_____

_____

*(Use another sheet of paper if you run out of room to answer the questions.)*

# A Salute to You, the Reader

You bought this manual and now you have finished reading it. That shows responsibility; you really care about improving your sexual life.

# Congratulations!

You have the initiative it takes to change. I realize you are probably very busy, but I assure you, put a little time aside each day and watch it turn into major accomplishments.

Review this manual often. If your sex life starts getting routine, go back and find something to do that you've never tried before. Keep the book handy so you can refer to it often.

Good luck in your adventure to improve your sex life within your marriage. May the Lord bless your relationship. Remember, you are already twice blessed if you have a man who loves you.

The sexes were made for each other, and only in the wise and loving union of the two is the fullness of health and duty and happiness to be expected.

-*William Hall*

## References

Some of this research is not well documented in support of the X-tasy Spot, while some other references are very valid.

*This list of references is supplemented by a brief description of each source.*

Heli Alzate (1985). "Vaginal Eroticism: A Replication Study." *Archives of Sexual Behavior*, 14 (6), 529-537. This article found that the G spot, located on the upper front interior wall of the vagina, is just one spot that results in orgasm for the woman. The back wall of the vagina is also an important source of sexual pleasure. Most women are sensitive on both walls of the vagina. If a woman is particularly sensitive on the back wall, she is likely to be able to achieve an orgasm through stimulation of her anus and rectum as well.

Bryce Britton (January IV81). "Grafenberg Spot." *Omni*, p. 36. This is a short review of G spot research. It shows that uterine orgasms can be measured.

Winifred Gallagher (February, 1986). "The Etiology of Orgasm." *Discover*, pp. 51-59. This is a nice review of a number of studies. It is based on the premise that most of sex is indeed in the head. This viewpoint is substantiated to an extent but leaves open the question of the role of physical stimulation. Remember that the X-tasy Spot is not in your head, it is in your vagina.

Alice Kahn Ladas, Beverly Whipple, and John D. Perry (1982). *G Spot and Other Recent Discoveries About Human Sexuality*. New York: Holt, Rinehart & Winston. This book compiles research findings on the G spot. It seriously discusses the implications of these findings for each woman. It discusses sex in ordinary language, explaining any technical terms.

E. R. Mahoney (1983). *Human Sexuality*. New York: McGraw-Hill. This book explains the female orgasm in detail. It is a useful treatment of the subject. Among its subjects are the following: the cervix's role in the orgasmic experience, the role of the uterus in this experience, and the woman's capacity to experience multiple orgasms.

William H. Masters, Virginia E. Johnson and Robert C. Kolodny (1988). *Human Sexuality* (3rd ed.). Glenview, IL: Scott, Foresman. This is the latest edition of the 1966 landmark book by Masters and Johnson. In the intervening two decades, these authors have not changed their position on the clitoral orgasm being the only orgasm.

Michael D. Newcomb and P. M. Bentler (1983). "Dimensions of Subjective Female Orgasmic Responsiveness." *Journal of Personality and Social Psyshology*, 44 (4), 862-873. This scholarly study of the sexual experience takes into account the possibility that women have different and subjective perceptions of their orgasm. This is a highly technical paper, but it can be scanned for its main points. In particular, the issue of whether a more than one kind of orgasm exists is raised. The evidence on this point is contradictory.

Avodah K. Offit, "Your Sexual Self." *Glamour*. This monthly column, beginning with the August 1982 issue of *Glamour*, confronts directly whether the clitoris is the only source of orgasm for a woman. It suggests that the blended orgasm, proposed by Singer, is the best, and that, therefore, the clitoris is not the only source of orgasm. The first installment concludes with a paragraph on dealing with conflicts. The following comment is worthy of quote: "Living together as adults involves the ability to compromise and adapt skills we can only acquire by understanding each other as deeply as we care for each other."

John Delbert Perry and Beverly Whipple (1981). "Pelvic Muscle Strength of Female Ejaculators: Evidence in Support of a New Theory of Orgasm." *The Journal of Sex Research*, 17(1), 22-39. This article presents the continuum conception of female orgasms, presented in Table 1. The authors have documented the presence of the G spot, as well as showing that ejaculation in females is a consequence of rubbing the G spot.

Lorna J. Sarrel and Philip M. Sarrel (1984). *Sexual Turning Points: The Seven Stages of Adult Sexuality*. New York: MacMillan. This book is sympathetic to the G spot theory. It also acknowledges that each woman is unique and can vary in her sexual responses over her lifetime. The authors say that "...the range of physiological reactions, feelings, and attitudes is very great."

Irving Singer (1973). *The Goals of Human Sexuality*. New York: Norton. This book coins the terms, "vulval orgasm," "uterine orgasm," and "blended orgasm." A description of each is provided so that the reader can compare her own experience to these descriptions.

Amy B. Taublieb and John R. Lick (1986). "Female Orgasm Via Penile Stimulation: A Critique of Adequate Sexual Functioning." *Journal of Sex and Marital Therapy*, 12 (1), 60-64. This article shows that different methods of sexual stimulation can influence how the orgasm is felt and perceived. Penile stimulation and masturbation are seen as producing a similar intensity of pleasure, but the quality of the experience is different for each. The use of the penis has been restored to its former position of importance. Relationships are based on sharing, and this is best expressed during intercourse.

Carol Tavris and Susan Sadd (1977). *The Redbook Report on Female Sexuality: 100,000 Married Women Disclose the Good News about Sex* (2nd ed.). New York: Delacorte. This study of a nationwide sample of married women notes that men and women are more similar sexually than they are different. This means that when each experiences an orgasm, the description of the orgasm is practically indistinguishable from one sex to another.

## Additional Reading

Here is a list of books to help you as you endeavor to improve your relationship with your husband, especially your sex life:

### Adventures in Sex

*How to Drive Your Man Wild in Bed* by Graham Masterton.

*The Joy of Sex, A Gourmet Guide to Lovemaking* by Alex Comfort, M.B., Ph.D.

*The Man's/The Woman's Gourmet Sex Book*, both books by Peggy and Evan Burke.

*A Woman's Little Black Book of Romantically Crazy Ideas* by Heidi Larsen.

*Sexual Energy, Ecstasy, A Practical Guide to Lovemaking: Secrets of the East and West* by David and Ellen Ramsdal

*The G Spot and Other Recent Discoveries* by Alice Kahn Ladas, Beverly Whipple, and John D. Perry

*ESO—How You and Your Lover Can Give Each Other Hours of "Extended Sexual Orgasm"* by Alan P. Brauer, M.D. and Donna J. Brauer.

*Why Men Don't Get Enough Sex and Women Don't Get Enough Love* by Jonathan Kramer, Ph.D. and Diane Dunaway.

*How To Make Love All the Time* by Barbara DeAngelis, Ph.D.

*How To Have an Orgasm . . . As Often As You Want* by Rachel Swift

*Super Sexual Orgasm* by Barbara Keesling, Ph.D.

*Talk Sexy To The One You Love* by Barbara Keesling, Ph.D.

*How To Make Love All Night* by Barbara Keesling, Ph.D.

### Relationships

*How One of You Can Bring the Two of You Together* by Susan Page

*Men Are from Mars, Women Are from Venus* by John Gray, Ph.D.

*Mars and Venus in The Bedroom* by John Gray, Ph.D.

## For the Man

*Male Multiple Orgasm: Step by Step* by Jack Johnston
(Seminar and audio cassette) Phone: 800-349-9866 (Web Site)
www.multiples.com

# Add Your Own List of Self-improvement Books

# Diary and/or New Sex Play
# the Two of You Invented

_____

_____

_____

_____

_____

_____

_____

_____

_____

_____

_____

_____

_____

_____

_____

_____

_____

_____

_____

_____

_____

# New Ideas

Did this book give you any new suggestions for improving sex?

☐ yes ☐ no

If yes, what are some of the new ideas you and your partner might find exciting? Try to list at least 10 things.

_____

_____

_____

_____

_____

_____

_____

_____

_____

_____

_____

_____

_____

_____

_____

_____

_____

_____

# Commitment

Will you commit to incorporating at least one sex play variation per month for the next year to add excitement and spice to your sex life?

☐ yes ☐ no

*If yes, sign below:*

I, _____ ,
will try something new and exotic during lovemaking at least 12 times this year to enhance the quality of my sex life.

Date:

_____

## ♥ Afterword ♥

Throughout the year I hope you refer to this book for helpful suggestions on having a fulfilling and satisfying love life.

In order to keep the 101 Erotic Things to Do and the Love Games as a surprise for your man, give him the following tear-out section instead of the whole book.

## Sex Pilot Checklist

♥

## Locating the X-tasy Spot

### Planning:

☐ *Briefing* ..........Discuss the X-Spot with her. Make sure that she's checked with her gynecologist first.

☐ *Foreplay* .............Beginning at dinner the night before.

### Pre-Flight:

☐ *Clean* ...............Shower/shave/brush teeth. Use a cologne that is her favorite.

☐ *Fingernails* .............Short, Clean, and Smooth.

### Clearance:

☐ *Wife* .................... Receive clearance for takeoff. (Be sure she knows that this experience this time is just for her. She is not expected to reciprocate sexually for now; just enjoy and maybe coach you a little about what feels good and what doesn't.)

### Takeoff:

☐ *Oil-Pressure* ............. Yes, lots of sex oil.

☐ *Foreplay* ................. Complete (back rub, foot rub, the works).

☐ *Climax* ................... Recommended and very likely.

☐ *Procedure* ................ With her on her back, kneel beside her and, with your palm upward, insert two or three fingers, leaving at least the little finger and thumb out and bent over.

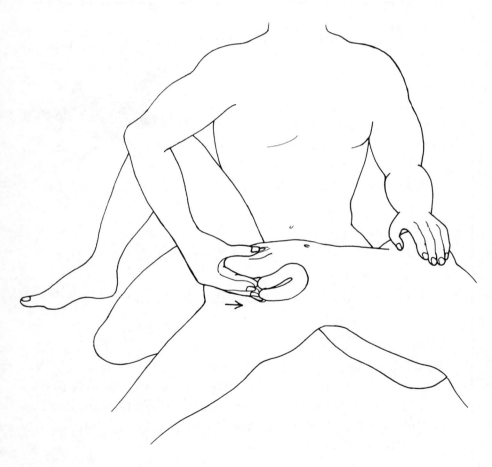

## Climb:

Begin by spreading her legs and inserting two or three fingers palm upward into the vagina. At the end of the tunnel, you will find a hard, rounded lump with a depression or indentation in the middle of the protrusion. This is the cervix, on which the X-Spot is located.

As you deeply probe the vagina, you can fondle the cervix with your fingers. Pressing firmly, as though massaging, is the key to cervical gratification. You can rub your fingers on this X-Spot or around the side of it to gently move the lump back and forth. Lightly rubbing or tapping the indentation of the cervix, increasing pressure in small increments, is one way to find the pleasure point.

Gentlemen, you must be careful not to push on the cervix too hard. As she begins to have an orgasm, there's no need to increase speed or pressure on the cervix. The same pressure used to initiate orgasm will be sufficient to keep it going. Pushing harder or faster could cause pain, spoiling the effect. Your fingers can rub and gently move the X-spot as your thumb stimulates the clitoris. Your other hand is free to caress her nipples and other sensitive spots.

While fondling your wife's X-Spot, if at any time during her orgasm you feel contractions, that's okay; it's part of the body's reflex. Other times you may feel a widening of the vagina barrel. That is normal also, and it is called "tenting."

## CRUISE:

☐ *Listen* .................. Have her rate what she feels on a scale of one to ten while you experiment with the X-Spot.

☐ *Expect* .................. A long orgasmic flight.

### *Descent:*

☐ *Safety* .................... If you notice that there is bleeding before ever having removed your hand, stop and tell her. She should check with her doctor before you try again.

If after removing your hand there is only a small amount of blood and the bleeding has stopped, you can wait to tell after she's come down, so she can ask her doctor about it.

☐ *Landing* .................. Only when she runs out of orGASm.

## Variations of the X-tasy Spot Rub

Here are descriptions and illustrations of many ways to perform the X-tasy Spot rub. You're sure to find a few that work best for you.

The drawing below is a cutaway view of the female anatomy that shows the different ways the X-tasy Spot can be stimulated. Manually rubbing and gently moving the cervix by hand is the most direct way to give your spouse hour-long orgasms.

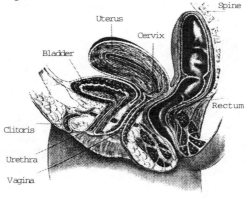

On the next few pages, four techniques are illustrated:

- Love Slide
- X-Massage
- Love Tug
- Love Triangle

## Love Slide

Slide three fingers into the vagina to teasingly bump and caress the tip of the cervix.

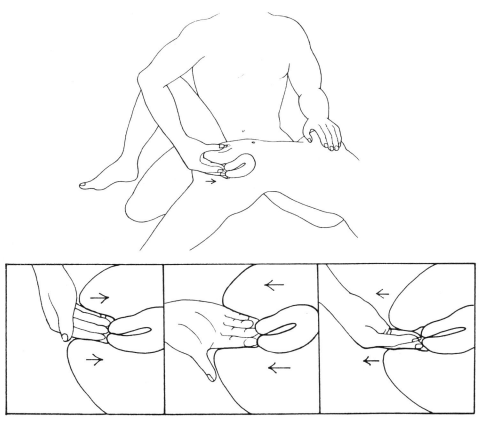

# X-Massage

Find the indentation at the end of the cervix and gently probe it with the middle finger. Then run your finger around the rim. Move the cervix gently back and forth with the finger pressed into the indentation.

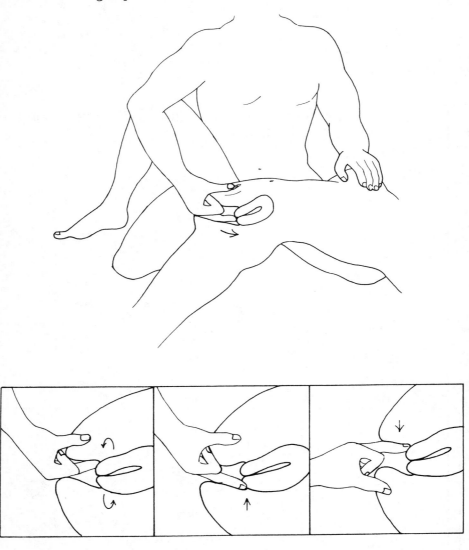

# Love Tug

Lovingly tug on the side of the cervix moving it back and forth and side to side. Always strive for gentle movement of the uterus.

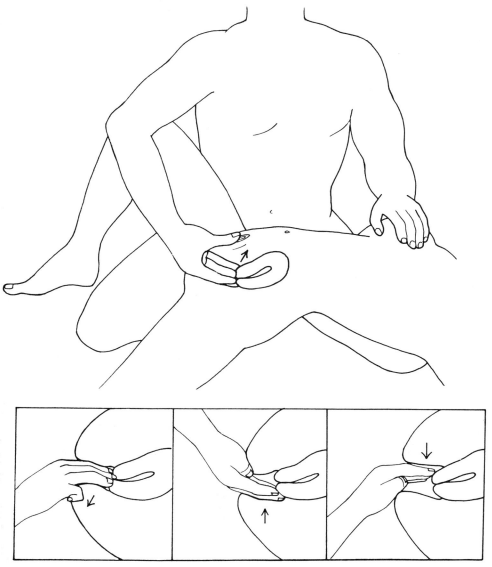

# Love Triangle

Encompass the cervix with three fingers. Move your hand in circles and rotate for the desired effect.

The woman can be face up or face down. If she is face up, your thumb can stimulate the clitoris. Squeezing the pubic bone with a finger stimulates the G spot while the other three fingers work on the X-tasy Spot.

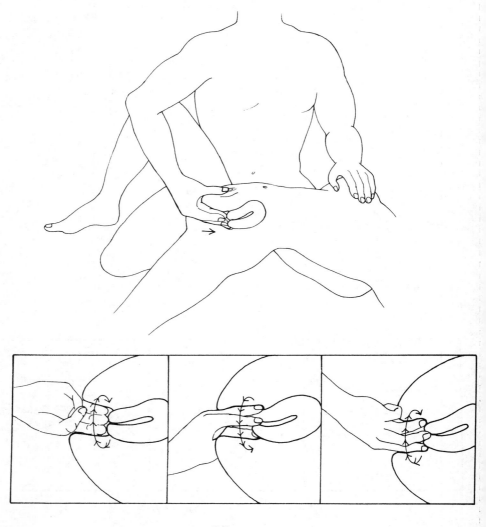

# Face Down, Manual Stimulation

Face down, the pinkie manipulates the clitoris. The ring finger pummels the G spot, the middle and index fingers work the X-tasy Spot, and the thumb can probe the anus.

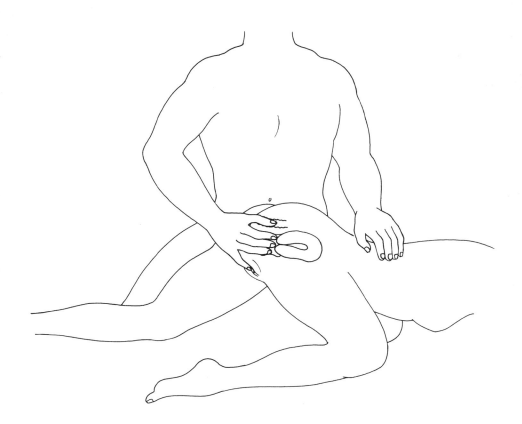

# Horizontal Slide Technique

Many sexual positions will stimulate the X-tasy Spot if done properly. Ordinarily, the man thrusts his penis in and out during sexual intercourse. To affect the X-tasy Spot, he must make love differently.

In the Horizontal Slide Technique, the penis is thrust deep inside the woman's vagina; then a horizontal sliding motion by the man, forward-backward, causes the penis to bend up and down, bumping the cervix back and forth.

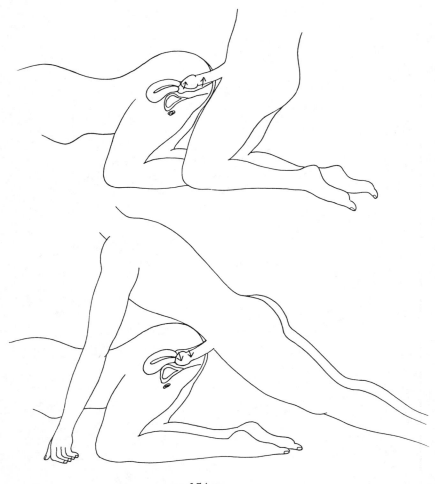

Start by putting your wife on her stomach, face down. (You may want to start this position with her kneeling instead.) Enter your wife's vagina from behind, either kneeling or lying on top of her. Once you have deep penetration, you then push up toward her head and slide back toward her feet. You keep your body straight, not pumping with your hips in the ordinary way. At the same time, angle your wife's buttocks up as far as you can. A pillow placed under her hips can help. This is a pleasant position because you can caress your spouse's breasts or clitoris from behind.

For more power, push on your wife's underarms to slide toward her feet, and by having your wife bend her knees, push off the back of her knees with your heels to slide toward her head.

You need only to slide up and down horizontally while your wife adjusts the angle. A pillow will help her hold the angle once she has found it. In this way, you are in the power and speed position, while she fine-tunes herself to put all your effort in just the right X-tasy Spot.

# X-tasy Spot Horizontal Slide Technique

Penis bends down, rubs across end of cervix to the "maximum up" position. In the "maximum down" position, penis is on top of cervix.

To slide in horizontally, push with legs by locking heels behind her knees; to slide out, push with arms at her shoulder. Sliding motion causes penis to bend up and down. As the penis pivots on the man, it bumps the cervix back and forth causing a full feeling.

*Heels locked behind knees*

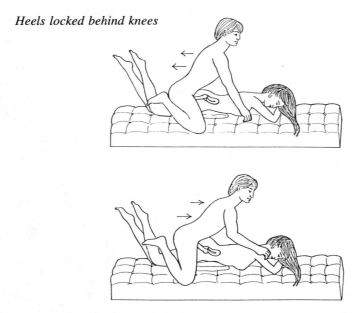

# Positions

### *Male from Behind:*

There are a variety of positions you can use during one session of lovemaking that hit the X-tasy Spot, although, I must admit, ladies do not have to move too much to experience an explosive orgasm from an X-tasy Spot rub.

Start out with woman kneeling with hands on the bed. The man kneels behind and enters vagina from behind. Once in, he slides back and forth, not in and out.

This is a great penetration angle. He can hold her hips and bring her in deeper. The man has lots of control and leverage in this position and has access to her breasts and clitoris in this position.

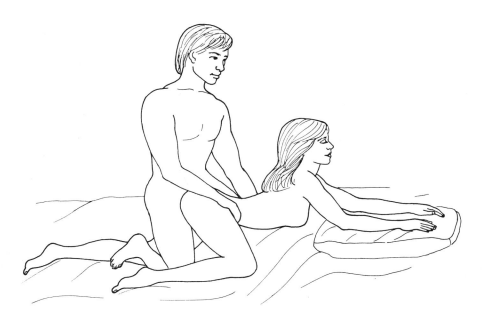

# Positions

Start out with woman kneeling with hands on bed. Man kneels behind and enters vagina from behind.

This is a great penetration angle. He can hold her hips and bring her in deeper. The man has lots of control and leverage in this position.

The man has access to her breasts and clitoris in this position.

## Best X-tasy Spot Rub Position

Notice the pillow under her hips to access the right angle.

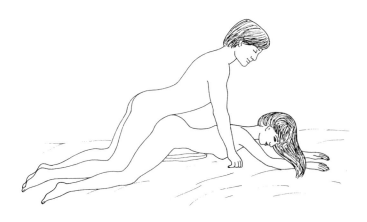

# Ecstasy — X-tasy Spot Orgasm

Elbows on bed, pillow under hips. Knees are bent, legs up, and head is facing forward and up.